HEALT
EATI

Alison Forbes is a freelance health writer and journalist. She has a particular interest in complementary medicine and children's issues. She writes regularly for a variety of publications including *Here's Health*, *Under Five*, *Parents* and *Mizz*. She has previously published an English textbook. Alison Forbes lives in North London with her family.

HEALTHY EATING

Cooking with Vitamins and Minerals

•

Alison Forbes

PENGUIN BOOKS

PENGUIN BOOKS
Published by the Penguin Group
27 Wrights Lane, London W8 5TZ, England
Viking Penguin Inc., 40 West 23rd Street, New York, New York 10010, USA
Penguin Books Australia Ltd, Ringwood, Victoria, Australia
Penguin Books Canada Ltd, 2801 John Street, Markham, Ontario, Canada L3R 1B4
Penguin Books (NZ) Ltd, 182–190 Wairau Road, Auckland 10, New Zealand

Penguin Books Ltd, Registered Offices: Harmondsworth, Middlesex, England

First published 1990
1 3 5 7 9 10 8 6 4 2

The Tables used in this book are Crown Copyright and are reproduced with
the permission of the Royal Society of Chemistry on behalf of the Controller of
Her Majesty's Stationery Office

Printed in England by Clays Ltd, St Ives plc
Filmset in Lasercomp Photina 10½/13 pt

For Graeme, Hannah and Sean
with all my love

ACKNOWLEDGEMENTS

Extra special thanks to my technical consultant, computer whizzkid Sid Verber, without whose help, advice and support this book would never have reached the publisher.

Special thanks to Paul Redgate, Quality Controller at Booker Health, for his unending patience in supplying food table information.

Special thanks to Patrick Holford, Director of the Institute for Optimum Nutrition, for reading over the text and making constructive comments.

Particular thanks to all my friends and recipe testers (some of whom succumbed under pressure!), for all the time and effort put into testing recipes and making useful comments.

USEFUL INFORMATION

Tables

The tables are taken from the fourth edition of McCance and Widdowson's THE COMPOSITION OF FOODS by Paul and Southgate; its second supplement, IMMIGRANT FOODS (HMSO) by Tan, Wenlock and Buss, both published by HMSO; and its third supplement, CEREALS AND CEREAL PRODUCTS, by Holland, Unwin and Buss. The third and subsequent supplements to THE COMPOSITION OF FOODS update the earlier values and are being published by the Royal Society of Chemistry in cooperation with the Ministry of Agriculture, Fisheries and Food.

Additional information is provided from HANDBOOK OF THE NUTRITIONAL CONTENTS OF FOODS, prepared by Watt and Merrill for the US Department of Agriculture. The food items from this publication are marked with a *.

Further information is from FOOD COMPOSITION AND NUTRITION TABLES 1986/7, third edition by Souci, Fachmann and Kraut, kindly provided by Booker Health. The food items from this publication are marked with a **.

Measurements

Imperial measurements are given with metric in brackets. The conversion rates are approximate, so only work to one set of measures – no mixing of ounces and grammes. Teaspoons and tablespoons are always level measures, so

1 teaspoon = 5 ml
1 tablespoon = 15 ml

CONTENTS

1
·
GENERAL
INTRODUCTION
·

The importance of vitamins and minerals to health – especially their role in the prevention and cure of illness – has, at last, been recognized. In spite of the awareness that we should increase their content in our diet, most of us have only a limited knowledge of the vitamin and mineral contents of foods, and we may be unaware of the potentially adverse effects of pollution, farming methods, irradiation of foods, etc., on our vitamin and mineral intake.

I have endeavoured to provide you with more than a schoolbook knowledge of vitamins and minerals and their role in maintaining good health. I hope to increase your awareness by providing food tables to enable you to compile your own recipes, and I have tried to encourage good practice in the storage, preparation and cooking of food in order to ensure that you maximize your vitamin and mineral intake.

The book is aimed at both those who are already interested in healthy eating and those who are, perhaps, less committed but have recognized, nevertheless, that their diets should be improved.

I have tried to make the recipes as varied as possible, to cater for all tastes. My style of cooking is very much influenced by living in cosmopolitan London and by foreign travel, as well as by my belief that humans are meant to be omnivores, that is, we are meant to eat a wide range of foods, including meat, fish, dairy produce, fruit and vegetables, with the emphasis on the latter.

Good eating habits are about balance and moderation: if you eat red meat, you should limit your intake and try to buy organic produce; if you are concerned about pesticides, you should buy organic vegetables; if you cook with butter occasionally, as I do, you should reduce your saturated fat intake elsewhere. Healthy eating can sometimes be a difficult ideal to achieve in our busy lives and we all have to make compromises. Above all, eating is to be enjoyed and shared. So I hope you will have fun using the book and will feel healthier as a result!

2
·

HOW TO USE
THE BOOK
·

The book is divided into chapters according to different vitamins or minerals. If you want to know about calcium, for
example, you will find plenty of information in the calcium
chapter. Then there is a list of foods containing calcium from
which you will be able to compile your own favourite recipes.

The recipes

The recipes in each chapter have one vitamin or mineral as
their theme. Those in the calcium chapter, for example,
contain calcium, and those in the zinc chapter contain zinc.
Of course, they all contain other nutrients too so, since most
foods are rich in more than one vitamin or mineral, I have
had to select the chapter in which to place them. You will be
able to cross-reference for yourself, by using the tables and
the index.

When compiling the recipes, I have used ingredients for
which information is available in the food tables of textbooks.
Some foods included, that are rich in vitamins and minerals,
are not necessarily the most healthy in other respects. For
example, cheese and beef, both rich in zinc, are also high in
saturated fat and calories. I hope that you will eat foods of this
kind in moderation and that you will gradually change your
diet to include many of the healthier alternatives (for which
food tables may not be available), to take account of the

government reports on reducing fat and sugar intake, increasing fibre, etc.

The tables

Each chapter contains a table showing the vitamin and mineral content of selected foods. You will see on pp. 24–5, for example, a list of foods containing calcium, from which you will be able to compile your own recipes. A very simple calcium meal, for instance, could be whitebait fried in vegetable oil, with cheese melted on top, served with steamed kale.

The tables should only be used as a rough guide to food contents and not as a basis for any special diets, except under the guidance of a nutritionist or doctor. Methods of analysis and interpretation of results vary considerably from country to country, and the vitamin and mineral content of foods, as eaten, depends very much on how the food is stored, prepared and cooked (see later in the chapter). It also depends on the quality of the soil in which the food is grown, where the animals have grazed and whether they have been fed supplements. This means that there are enormous variations in vitamin and mineral contents for the same foods. Seasonal variations also have to be taken into account.

Some of the foods mentioned in the recipes have not been listed in the tables, due to lack of space. Anyone wishing to check these or any of the items marked * or ** should refer to the publications from which the tables have been taken (see p. viii).

3

•

GETTING ENOUGH
VITAMINS
AND MINERALS

•

It is practically impossible to tell if you are getting enough vitamins and minerals because signs of deficiency do not usually manifest themselves until months after they occur, and symptoms are often very vague and non-specific. For instance, you may feel lethargic, apathetic and depressed most of the time, but this could be symptomatic of a shortage of any number of vitamins. Furthermore, each individual has different requirements that change all the time according to circumstances. The ability to absorb and utilize nutrients also varies.

Stress, smoking and all the features of our modern lifestyles contribute to vitamin and mineral deficiencies. This means that we are all likely to be affected by vitamin and mineral losses at some time in our lives and it is doubtful whether we ever make them up. Our deficiencies are then passed on to the next generation.

Despite its appearance, the quality of our food has deteriorated in many respects over the last decade. Modern farming methods leave the soil depleted of minerals; the use of pesticides and nitrates in the soil, and antibiotics given to animals, affect the biochemistry of our bodies and thus our vitamin and mineral intake. The more toxic products we consume, the more nutrients we need to detoxify ourselves. We demand convenient, well-packaged produce but the processing may leave food devoid of nutrients. The effects of irradiation, now introduced in Britain, are still unclear.

There have been numerous reports, from government departments and independent bodies, showing that in Britain the average diet falls well short of the recommended intake of vitamins and minerals. Given that these Recommended Daily Allowances (RDAs) are a minimum amount, this means many people simply are not getting enough nutrients.

One study, 'The Diets of British Schoolchildren', published by the former Department of Health and Social Security (DHSS) in 1986, showed that the vast majority of British schoolchildren were below the DHSS's RDA for iron.

Another study, published in 1980 by the DHSS, showed that pre-school children had an average intake lower than the RDAs for vitamins B_1, B_2 and B_3 and a smaller number showed low intakes of vitamins A and D.

A report from the National Advisory Committee on Nutrition Education (NACNE) in 1983 pointed out that 'perhaps 10 per cent of households have been estimated to consume less than 30 mg of vitamin C per head' and 'up to 14 per cent of elderly groups surveyed when over seventy years of age have been found to have clear evidence of folic acid deficiency'.

The Booker Health report, published in 1985, showed that many people's intake of vitamin A and folic acid was below the RDA and the US RDA for vitamin B_6. Women in particular showed low intakes of folic acid, iron and calcium. Many people were below the recommended levels for iron, calcium and zinc.

It makes sense, therefore, to improve your vitamin and mineral intake immediately through diet, by buying good quality food and preparing and cooking it in such a way as to keep vitamin and mineral losses to a minimum.

Recommended Daily Allowances –
Why do they provide so little help?

If you have looked at the packaging of your food lately, you may have noticed under 'nutritional information' that the carrots you have bought provide x per cent of the recommended daily allowance (RDA) for vitamin A. The trouble is that this is misleading for a variety of reasons. The RDAs, set in Britain by the Committee on the Medical Aspects of Food Policy (COMA), are not designed for individuals. They are set quite specifically for *population groups*. They are defined in the 1979 COMA report as 'the average amounts of a nutrient which should be provided per head in a group of people if the needs of practically all members of the group are to be met'. Nor are they really intended for use by the public. They are meant to be used by nutritionists, dieticians and other professionals for many aspects of their work, including planning national food supplies, planning therapeutic diets or institutional meals and assessing food intake of groups.

Another problem is that RDAs vary from country to country. Sometimes these variations are enormous, even where amounts are intended for people with similar lifestyles. For example, in Britain, the RDA for calcium is 500 mg, whereas in the USA it is 800 mg. You also find that one country may have an RDA for a particular vitamin or mineral, and another country does not have one.

In Britain, there are only RDAs for vitamin A, thiamine, riboflavin, niacin, vitamins C and D, calcium and iron. There are currently no RDAs for vitamins B_6, B_{12}, pantothenic acid, biotin, E and K and the minerals chlorine, potassium, magnesium, manganese, chromium, cobalt, copper, iodine, molybdenum, phosphorus, selenium and zinc.

The British RDA for folic acid, set in 1979 at 300 micrograms, was withdrawn in 1981. In the light of the evidence that an adequate intake of folic acid in a mother's diet helps to prevent spina bifida, this would appear to be a misguided decision, especially as the so-called average British diet was found to provide less than half that daily amount at 105 micrograms.

In the USA, the National Research Council also make recommendations for several more vitamins and minerals: vitamins B_6 and B_{12}, folic acid, vitamin E, magnesium, zinc, phosphorus and iodine. But even this list only represents sixteen out of the twenty-six vitamins and minerals known to be essential for normal body function.

The US figures do not, for instance, include selenium or chromium. Yet there is increasing epidemiological evidence that selenium is important for the prevention of heart attacks and cancer, and recent studies show the importance of chromium as a constituent part of the glucose tolerance factor in the prevention of diabetes.

How can we account for these differences? Some of them may be due to specific uncertainties about different nutrients. For example, no one is quite sure how much vitamin D an individual can synthesize from sunlight, so it is very difficult to come up with an RDA that would suit everybody.

For vitamin C, experts disagree how much is necessary to keep the body tissues saturated. The maximum body pool for vitamin C, that is, keeping the body tissues saturated, is about 1500 mg. To set the RDA, it has to be decided whether to keep the pool topped up to its maximum or to keep the limit to half or one-third of that. The USA has opted for an RDA of 60 mg; in Britain it is 30 mg. It is tempting to suggest that the differences between countries are more to do with bureaucratic or political decisions than scientific evidence. That does not help us very much.

The RDAs in Britain have not been updated since 1979, yet our lifestyles and the kind of food we eat have changed drastically since then. COMA is currently examining the present RDAs to see if any changes are necessary. It is studying all the vitamins and minerals deemed to be essential and a report will be published in 1991. But the bureaucratic machinery takes so long that by the time new RDAs are set, our deficiencies will be well-established.

In the USA, the National Research Council is proposing an increase in some vitamins, notably vitamins C and A, to incorporate preventive measures against cancer. It remains to be seen whether Britain will adopt the idea of preventive measures of this sort.

Another major failing of RDAs – one with which health industries in particular take issue – is that they are an absolute *minimum amount*. A huge margin of safety is included to allow for individual differences and to prevent the possibility of intake at toxic levels. For example, the RDA for vitamin C, set at 30 mg, is the least you can consume to prevent you getting scurvy.

The health food industries encourage us to take vitamin and mineral supplements. Many independent experts recommend optimum ranges for vitamins and minerals that are much, much higher than the RDAs set by governments. These optimum ranges are set to allow us to achieve *optimum health*, rather than just the prevention of disease. There is clear evidence that better intake of vitamins and minerals can improve our performance in all walks of life, but governments are very concerned about the increase in consumption of vitamin and mineral supplements. They are worried about the possibilities of excesses and concerned that health food industries may make all sorts of claims about their products. Indeed, without professional guidance, it is practically impossible to know how many supplements would be appropriate for any given individual.

Governments, in their discussions about RDAs, may well come up with several different levels in the future, to cater more widely for individual variations: a lower diagnostic level to be used by health professionals in their work; a prescriptive figure for the general public (that is, a figure or range that people are advised to use as a rule); and an upper level above which risks of adverse side-effects from high intake start.

Meanwhile, what are we to do? Most of us want more than the knowledge that vitamin C will stop us getting

9

scurvy. We now expect to lead full, healthy lives with increased longevity and a reduction in degenerative diseases. In other words, we expect and have a right to health, as defined by the World Health Organization (WHO) – 'a state of complete physical, mental and social well-being and not merely the absence of disease'.

The COMA report is not much help when it says: 'since the distribution of requirements for nutrients is not known, it is not possible to estimate the probability that an individual is undernourished by comparing his or her intake with the recommended amount'. In effect, this means that RDAs are at present of little use to us. As individuals, we have no real way of knowing whether we are getting enough vitamins and minerals. When we read that our carrots contain x per cent of the RDA, we are not really any the wiser.

We must put pressure on governments to come up with RDAs that are more helpful to individuals, and insist that they exert pressure on food manufacturers to be more specific in their food labelling.

Maximizing our Vitamin and Mineral Intake

We have little control over commercial processing of foods, but we *can* demand fresh, organically-grown produce that has been stored in our supermarkets and shops in such a way as to minimize vitamin and mineral losses. It is then up to us to ensure we maximize our intake by storing, preparing and cooking the food properly.

STORAGE

Once fruit and vegetables are picked, or they become overripe, enzymes which helped synthesize vitamins during growth start their destructive action and the loss of vitamins is accelerated. These enzymes thrive at room temperature, with light and oxygen, but their action is inhibited by heat, cold and acid conditions. As soon as you get vegetables home, wash, dry and refrigerate them in airtight conditions to prevent enzymic action.

Salad vegetables should be refrigerated unwashed, as washing may cause damage to their thin leaves or skins.

Vegetables with thick skins, such as swedes, potatoes or turnips, may have some protection against light and air, but they should be stored in a cool, dark place and used as soon as possible. Potatoes, in particular, lose their vitamin C content very quickly at room temperature, and all vegetables left in the light at room temperature rapidly lose their vitamin A, B_2 and C content.

Fruits with good protective skins, such as citrus fruits, apples and bananas, can be kept at room temperature but should not be stored for too long since they lose their vitamin content once they are overripe. Guavas, for example, lose 80 per cent of their vitamin C once ripe.

Soft fruit should go in the fridge unwashed as handling may cause bruising, which starts the enzymic process.

Fruit juices, once opened, should be refrigerated in an airtight container. They should not be shaken as this accelerates the oxidation process.

OTHER FOODS

Milk exposed to sunlight loses its riboflavin (B_2) content at a rate of 10 per cent per hour. Bottled milk, stored under bright lights in the supermarket, can lose its riboflavin in 20 minutes. Once riboflavin is destroyed, it leaves a product called lumiflavin that destroys vitamin C; milk should therefore be refrigerated as soon as possible and perhaps be bought only in cartons.

Preparation and Cooking

The best way to increase your vitamin and mineral intake is unquestionably to eat raw, fresh fruit and vegetables, but obviously this is not always practical.

Poor cooking and preparation methods probably cause

the greatest losses of vitamins and minerals, especially from vegetables. The worst losses occur at high temperatures, with long cooking times and an excessive amount of water.

Stir-frying is one of the best methods for cooking vegetables because, although it is at high temperatures, it is quick, and any vegetable juices leached out are retained. Steaming is also good because little water is used and, provided there is a tight-fitting lid and the heat is kept low so that no steam can escape, the nutrients may be reabsorbed into the food by the time it is cooked.

Microwave cooking of meat, poultry, fruit and vegetables has much the same effect on vitamins and minerals as other cooking methods. Because microwaves use little water to cook fruit and vegetables, leaching is kept to a minimum. When used for reheating, microwaves cause little additional destruction of vitamins and minerals, resulting in fewer losses.

Keeping food warm for a long time causes further losses. Three-quarters of the vitamin content of a meal may be lost if the food is kept for several hours. The quicker the food moves from preparation to the table, the better.

PREPARATION
Here are a few tips for preparing and cooking vegetables:

- Wash thoroughly in cold water. Never soak.
- Scrub root vegetables gently. Never scrape.
- Cut while still chilled.
- Keep chopping, slicing or shredding to a minimum to avoid oxidation.
- Once cut, use as soon as possible.
- Toss already cut salad vegetables in a little lemon juice to prevent discoloration and oxidation. Use immediately.
- Peel only when absolutely essential.
- Save peelings for soup if you are satisfied they have not been polluted.
- Use tops, for example, turnip or carrot, for soups.

- Sprout your seeds to increase the vitamin and mineral content.

COOKING

- Steam vegetables for preference. Cover the pan tightly. Always retain the cooking water.

- If boiling, use as little water as possible. Bring boiling water to the vegetables. Cover the pan tightly. Retain cooking water for stock.

- Cook until only just tender.

- Never add soda.

- The principles for cooking fruit are the same. Cook in the shortest possible time and serve in its own liquid to preserve nutrients. Fruit salad should always be prepared at the last minute. Once the fruit is cut, toss in a little lemon juice to prevent the harmful effects of oxidation.

- Toasting nuts and seeds considerably enhances their flavour but causes losses of vitamins and minerals.

GENERAL COOKING HINTS

- Don't use aluminium cookware because it may leave deposits of aluminium in your food. Copper cookware may also leave deposits especially when it reacts to acidic foods such as fruit.

- Keep all drips from thawing, juice from meat and liquids from tinned food for use in stock, sauce or soup.

- Keep pan or casserole lids on tightly.

- If braising, heat the oven and the casserole first.

- Stir-fry meat and other foods, for preference, to keep the cooking time short. Make sure the food is dry, or the oil will not stick. Ensure that the oil is very hot. Corn oil, peanut (groundnut) oil and soya oil are best for stir-frying because they can reach high temperatures without burning.

- Soak all beans, chickpeas and whole dried peas

overnight. Discard the soaking water, even though you may lose some vitamins and minerals. Cook in fresh water and fast-boil uncovered, for at least ten minutes, to get rid of toxins. (Soya beans should be boiled hard for one hour.) Then boil for the appropriate cooking time.

Useful additions to the diet

You are probably very familiar with the foods available in health shops. However, you may not have tried sea vegetables and sprouted seeds, both of which are an excellent source of vitamins and minerals that we cannot afford to ignore.

SPROUTED BEANS AND SEEDS

Sprouted beans and seeds contain all the essential nutrients: proteins, fats, carbohydrates, vitamins and minerals.

They contain significant quantities of vitamins. Because the sprouts are usually still growing when you eat them, provided they are fresh, there is minimal vitamin loss. Sprouted beans and seeds contain large quantities of vitamin C. They contain all the B vitamins, including the elusive B_{12}, which is of particular importance to vegetarians, since it is normally only found in foods of animal origin; they also contain significant quantities of vitamins A, D and E. Most sprouted beans and seeds contain plenty of minerals, in a form that is easily digested. Minerals include: calcium, iron, phosphorus, potassium and magnesium.

Unfortunately, information about the vitamin and mineral contents of sprouted seeds and beans is not readily available.

You can sprout practically any whole bean or seed and whole grains. Popular ones to try are: mung beans, soya beans, blackeye beans, flageolet beans and haricot beans; whole lentils, whole peas, chickpeas; fenugreek seeds, hulled sunflower seeds and pumpkin seeds; sesame seeds, alfalfa and wholewheat berries. (See Further Reading for details.)

14

SEA VEGETABLES

Sea vegetables are a major source of vitamins, minerals and trace elements that we cannot afford to ignore. In particular, they are a very good source of iodine, which is difficult to obtain other than from seafoods, and they contain small amounts of B_{12}, which is of particular importance to vegetarians. They are also a good source of protein and are low in calories.

Sea vegetables, unlike fish, tend not to absorb pollutants from the sea. In fact, they help to dispel radioactive and toxic wastes from the body. Our ancestors have always valued them for their health-giving properties.

They come in dried form, which means they can be stored for a long time. If they are unavailable in health shops, you can buy them by mail order. You may be put off by the smell at first, but once soaked, sea vegetables are like most other vegetables. Try them first in a soup, where their flavour blends in with the other ingredients. Then use them uncooked in a salad or serve as you would a green vegetable, with a main course. They come in all sorts of shapes, sizes and colours. Soak them according to instructions and they will expand considerably.

The most popular sea vegetables on sale here are:

Dulse. This grows in the North Atlantic and is eaten in Ireland, Canada and New England. It comes in purply-red strips and has a soft, slightly spicy flavour. It is rich in iron, potassium, magnesium, iodine and phosphorus and contains many B vitamins. It works well in soups or a salad and is good with grains or vegetables.

Wakame. This mild-tasting sea vegetable is very popular in Japan. It is rich in vitamin A, calcium, potassium and vitamin C and contains the B vitamins. It comes in dark brown strips and, once soaked, is good in soups, served with main courses or in a salad.

15

Arame. It comes in brown, stringy threads, grows around Japan and has a mild flavour that blends in well with others. It is rich in calcium, iodine, phosphorus, potassium, vitamin A and iron.

Nori (laver). This is a very popular sea vegetable because it is so easy to prepare. It usually comes in dried strips and, in Japan, is used to wrap around rice. In South Wales, it is usually eaten with oats as a thick purée called laverbread. It is a good source of iron and contains other minerals and B vitamins.

Kombu. It comes in thick, dark strips and is rich in calcium, phosphorus, potassium and iodine. It is traditionally used for cleansing the intestines and the Chinese use it for goitre. Kombu is also sold as kelp powder.

Carragheen. This grows on both sides of the Atlantic. It has light brown leaves that look a bit like tobacco and is rich in iodine, calcium, vitamin A and potassium. It has always been valued for clearing bronchial disorders. Carragheen can be used to set jellies and şavoury moulds, and as a thickener for soups, stews and sauces.

Agar. It comes in white flakes and as a green powder, and is rich in iodine and calcium. It can be used as a setting agent in fruit jellies and savoury moulds. I find the flakes easiest to use, but their setting properties tend to vary so it is advisable to follow the instructions on the packet; also to experiment. Agar has a neutral taste and, once dissolved, has no colour.

4
.

INTRODUCTION TO
MINERALS

.

Minerals or elements are, like vitamins, a major group of vital substances necessary to normal life. The minerals are divided into groups:

the macro- or gross elements. These minerals are present in relatively large amounts in the body and the daily requirements in our diet are several hundred milligrams. These are calcium, phosphorus, magnesium, sodium, potassium and chlorine.

the trace elements. These are required in very small quantities – a few milligrams a day. They include iron, zinc, copper, manganese, iodine, chromium, selenium, cobalt, molybdenum, sulphur and fluorine.

other important trace elements. There are many other trace elements that have an effect on our health and their role is being researched all the time. Some of these have been recognized as essential. Others have not been proved categorically essential but they do exert an influence over our bodies and our health. These include: vanadium, nickel, tin, lithium and other rare elements.

Experts disagree as to which of the lesser known elements are essential. In the past, there were quite clear guidelines for defining essentiality. Now, as more research is completed, the distinction between essential and beneficial, contaminating and polluting, is much hazier and I do not propose to enter the discussion here.

The role of minerals in the body

The macro-elements calcium, phosphorus and magnesium are involved in structural functions as constituents of the bones and teeth. Sodium and chlorine outside the cells, and phosphorus, magnesium and potassium inside the cells, help to control bodily fluids and serve in the transmission of nerve impulses.

The role of trace elements is essentially twofold: they function as activators for *enzymes*, the catalysts that are involved in so many bodily processes, and they activate *hormones*, the great controllers of the body that govern the action of enzymes.

The trace element iron has a unique function in its ability to carry oxygen from the lungs throughout the body. This is in the form of haemoglobin, the red pigment of the blood, and myoglobin, the pigment of muscle.

Minerals are supplied only in the food we eat, which means that ultimately, they come from the soil. If the soil is depleted of minerals, as it so often is nowadays, our intake from food will be reduced.

There is considerable interaction between all the different elements, both essential and toxic. They often compete with one another and if too much (or too little) of one mineral is absorbed, it can upset the balance. Most minerals are difficult to absorb apart from sodium, potassium, fluorine, iodine and chloride. Because everyone's absorption is different, and an individual's mineral status is dependent on so many factors, it is hard to assess how much each person needs.

REDUCTION OF MINERAL INTAKE

Minerals cannot be broken down but, like vitamins, they can be lost in food refining, processing and domestic cooking. The most significant loss of both macro- and trace minerals from food occurs during processing and refining, for example: the conversion of wholemeal flour to white; of wholegrain cereals to refined cereals; the polishing of brown, unpolished rice; the refining of raw cane and beet sugar into the white variety.

Minerals can also be immobilized by other naturally-occurring food constituents to form substances that are of no use to the body.

Phytates. Phytic acid is a naturally-occurring substance in the fibre content, that is, the raw bran, of wholemeal cereals. It attaches itself to certain minerals, notably iron, calcium, zinc and possibly magnesium, and stops them being absorbed by the body. These phytates are retained in many breakfast cereals containing raw bran, such as muesli and some uncooked oat products. Most experts agree, however, that if you eat no more than two heaped tablespoons of raw bran per day, your mineral intake should not be affected.

It seems that those on wholefood, vegetarian diets, who eat large amounts of raw grains, may be able to adapt to the amount of phytates in their diet, with the result that they are able to absorb the minerals which wholegrain cereals provide. It is thought, also, that the phytic acid and phytates in most wholemeal products are either destroyed by yeast in the leavening process involved in bread-making or by the high temperatures of baking. This means, on balance, that most people can take advantage of the minerals provided by raw bran. However, for those people who eat a lot of unleavened bread like chapatis, the effects of phytates are potentially devastating and those who eat a diet of junk food, which is already devoid of nutrients, should also be particularly careful.

Phytic acid is also present in other foods, especially soya products like TSP (textured soya protein). Soya beans contain phytates too, but it is thought that provided the beans are properly cooked, or allowed to sprout, the phytates present should be destroyed.

Phosphates. Phosphates added to many soft drinks can also inhibit the absorption of minerals such as calcium and iron.

Oxalates. Oxalates or oxalic acid also bind themselves to calcium and render it unabsorbable. These substances are found in many fruit and vegetables but are present in significant amounts in rhubarb, sorrel, spinach and beetroot as well as chocolate, tea, coffee and peanuts. It is thought that although the calcium absorption from these foods themselves may be inhibited, oxalates will not prevent the absorption of calcium from other foods.

Tannic acid. Tannin or tannic acid, rich in black tea, can also inhibit the absorption of iron and zinc, especially if the drink is taken with a meal.

Toxic metals. Toxic metals like lead and cadmium have a similar biochemical structure to some minerals, notably zinc. Because of this, they mimic its action in the body, but work against it by binding themselves to enzymes, preventing them from doing their work. This increases the body's needs for zinc. Lead also mimics iron, calcium, magnesium and copper, increasing the body's needs for these minerals.

5
.
CALCIUM
.

Calcium is the most abundant mineral in the body and 99 per cent of it is found in the bones and teeth, which act as a calcium store. The remaining 1 per cent, found in solution, helps with various biochemical functions.

Calcium is essential for the healthy development of bones and teeth in children and to maintain bone density in adults. It also has a vital role to play in the regulation of various body functions including normal nerve and muscle function, the control of cholesterol levels, regulation of the heart beat, assisting in the clotting of blood and keeping the blood pressure down.

The right calcium balance is absolutely essential for the maintenance of health. Calcium outside the body cells and magnesium within body cells work together to ensure the steady, smooth conduction of nerve impulses. If the balance is upset, as in magnesium deficiency, symptoms start to show. Similarly, calcium and phosphorus work together in the formation of bones and teeth. But many people eat a diet too rich in phosphorus, which affects the balance of the two minerals and means calcium cannot work properly. The ideal dietary ratio of calcium to phosphorus is $2:1$.

There are a large number of dietary substances that may inhibit the absorption of calcium: *phytates* in raw bran may prevent absorption, but this is now regarded as unlikely, provided you limit your intake to no more than two heaped tablespoons of raw bran per day.

Some foods, including spinach, sorrel, rhubarb and chocolate, contain *oxalates* or *oxalic acid* which prevents the body using the calcium they contain. These oxalates do not, however, prevent the absorption of calcium from other foods.

Phosphates, rich in a diet of junk or processed foods, may inhibit the absorption of calcium by upsetting the calcium: phosphorus ratio.

Alcohol may make it more difficult for the body to absorb calcium, and a diet high in *saturated fat* may prevent the body absorbing calcium because excess fat binds up the calcium in a form the body cannot use.

Other factors affecting your body's calcium status

Many other factors affect your calcium status:

- *A high protein diet* increases calcium loss in the urine so this may increase your need for calcium.

- *Vitamin D* enhances the absorption of calcium. It is synthesized in your skin in response to sunlight, so if you get plenty of sunshine, your calcium levels will be increased.

- *Exercise* increases the calcium store in your bones.

- If you do not eat enough *magnesium* in your diet, the calcium balance may be affected.

Signs of deficiency

Signs of deficiency include muscle cramps, fatigue, weakness, irritability, high blood pressure, periodontal disease such as gum recession and tooth loosening, and irregularities of the heart. Calcium deficiency can also lead to osteoporosis, a metabolic bone disease that causes the spine to curve and the bones to break easily. Osteoporosis affects both men and women, but it is usually associated with menopausal and

22

post-menopausal women. This is because levels of oestrogen, which helps the absorption of calcium, are greatly reduced around the time of the menopause.

THOSE MOST AT RISK OF DEFICIENCY

- Children, during periods of rapid skeletal growth, such as early infancy, and adolescence.

- People over thirty, when the body stops building bones and starts to concentrate on repairing and maintaining those that are already there.

- Pregnant women, because the developing foetus rapidly uses up the mother's supply of calcium.

- Breast-feeding women. If you breast-feed your baby for nine months, you lose four times as much calcium from your milk as you lost during nine months' pregnancy.

- Regular slimmers and those on elimination diets for allergies.

- Menopausal and post-menopausal women.

- The elderly.

Therapeutic uses

Some experts believe that large intakes of calcium, in the middle years of life, can help to prevent osteoporosis provided the calcium:magnesium balance is not upset. Too much calcium, however, can cause kidney problems such as kidney stones.

LOSSES FROM FOOD

Refining of flour causes considerable loss of calcium, but this is normally restored in white flour through fortification. *Heating milk* causes the soluble calcium to become insoluble and therefore less digestible. *Pasteurization* destroys an enzyme, phosphatase, that aids assimilation of calcium in the body.

Sources of calcium

Food	Mg per 100 g	Food	Mg per 100 g
Wakame	1,300 a	Almonds	250
Parmesan cheese	1,220	Kale, leaves only	249*
Skimmed milk powder	1,190	Soya beans	226
Arame	1,170 a	Watercress	220
Kelp	1,093*	Brewer's yeast	210*
Irish moss (carragheen)	885*	Soya flour	210
Whitebait, fried	860	Mussels, boiled	200
Cheddar cheese	800	Oysters	190
Agar, dried	756	Brazil nuts	180
Edam cheese	740	Haricot beans	180
Sprats, fried	710	Natural yoghurt	180
Blackstrap molasses	684*	Chinese leaves	154
Curry powder	640	Fenugreek leaves	150
Danish blue cheese	580	Prawns, boiled	150
Sardines, canned in oil, fish only	550	Chickpeas	140
Tofu, fried	530	Pistachio nuts	140
Tofu, steamed	507	Red kidney beans	140
Treacle	500	Spring onions, bulbs only	140
Sardines, canned in tomato sauce	460	Winkles, boiled	140
Vine leaves	391	Alfalfa	136*
Feta cheese	384	Sesame seeds	131
Camembert cheese	380	Cockles, boiled	130
Carob flour	352*	Egg yolk	130
White self-raising flour	350	Goat's milk	130
Parsley	330	Skimmed milk	130
Pilchards, canned in tomato sauce	300	Shrimps, frozen, shell removed	128
Anchovies, canned in oil, fish only	299	Bloater, grilled	120
		Cow's milk	120
Dulse	296*	Crab, canned	120
Dried figs	280	Horseradish	120
Fish paste	280	Muesli, Swiss style	120
		Scallops, steamed	120

Food	Mg per 100 g	Food	Mg per 100 g
Sunflower seeds	120*	Dried apricots	92
Blackeye beans	110	Mussels	88
Lemons	110	Red chillies	86
Wheat bran	110	Spring greens, boiled	86
Broad beans	104	Butter beans	85
Broccoli tops	100	Soy sauce, dark, thick	85
Fennel	100*	Aduki beans	83**
Mung beans	100	Dried yeast	80
Red pigeon peas	100	Globe artichoke	80
Rhubarb	100	Single cream	79
Cream cheese	98	Chinese mushrooms, dried	76
Currants	95	Savoy cabbage	75
Salmon, canned	93	Okra	70
Spinach	93		

Note:

a Information taken from *Vegetables from the Sea* by Teruko and Seibin Arasaki.

· *watercress salad* ·

serves 4

A simple salad for summer or winter.

3–4 tablespoons vinaigrette (see p. 239)
2 bunches watercress
4 spring onions
2 oz (56 g) alfalfa sprouts
2 oz (56 g) sunflower seeds

Make the dressing before you prepare the salad vegetables, to avoid loss of vitamins.

Remove any coarse stems from the watercress, put it in a salad-spinner drum, wash and spin dry. Thinly slice the onions, including the green bits. Separate the alfalfa sprouts, and mix them all together in a large salad bowl.

Sprinkle the sunflower seeds over the salad vegetables.

Toss the salad in vinaigrette until it is coated all over and serve immediately.

· *wakame salad* ·

serves 4–6

If you have never eaten sea vegetables, wakame's mild flavour makes it a good one to start with. You can find it in good health shops. It makes a green salad with a difference.

1½ oz (42 g) wakame (about three-quarters of a packet)

3–4 tablespoons vinaigrette or tangy dressing (see pp. 239, 241)

3 oz (84 g) alfalfa sprouts

3 sticks celery

3 oz (84 g) Chinese leaf

2 oranges

8 slices cucumber

3 oz (84 g) sunflower seeds

Soak the wakame for at least ten minutes in a large bowl of water and it will expand considerably. While waiting, make the dressing.

With scissors, cut or tear the fronds off the central vein. Discard the vein. Wash the leaves thoroughly, then pat dry with kitchen paper or spin-dry in a salad spinner and cut into small pieces.

Separate the alfalfa sprouts, finely slice the celery and cut the Chinese leaf thinly. (If you slice it downwards, it should fall away into thin strips.) Then cut into 1½ in (3.8 cm) lengths.

Peel the oranges and break into segments over the large salad bowl to catch the drips. Take off the pith, but do not discard. Chop into tiny pieces.

Thinly slice the cucumber and cut the slices in half.

Put all the ingredients in the bowl, plus the sunflower seeds, toss the salad in the dressing until it is thoroughly coated and serve immediately.

26

· sardine and spinach mousse ·

serves 4–6

Use an attractive jelly mould to set off this unusual green mousse. Agar flakes are slightly unpredictable in their setting properties. As a rough guide, use one part agar flakes to five parts liquid. You will find agar flakes in health shops.

---

1 lb (450 g) tender young spinach leaves
10 fl oz (300 ml) vegetable stock (including stock left after
  spinach is cooked)
2 tablespoons agar flakes (see instructions on packet)
2 free-range eggs, hardboiled
1 4½ oz (126 g) tin of sardines in oil
5 oz (140 g) natural low-fat set yoghurt
freshly ground black pepper

Garnish
fresh lemon wedges

Remove any coarse stems from the spinach. Wash the leaves and place in a large saucepan with any water that clings to the leaves. Cover and cook for 3–5 minutes until the spinach has wilted and is tender.

Drain the liquid into a measuring jug, retaining as part of the stock. Squeeze any surplus water out of the spinach into the jug with your hand. Chop the spinach finely and place in a medium-sized mixing bowl.

Put the stock in a saucepan, bring to the boil and add the agar flakes, stirring until they dissolve. Pour this liquid over the spinach, mixing it in, and leave to cool for about 10 minutes.

Shell the eggs and mash with a fork. Drain the sardines of oil and mash them with a fork, then mix both with the spinach when it has cooled.

Stir in the yoghurt and season with freshly ground black pepper. Pour the mixture into a 1½ pt (900 ml) jelly mould. Cover and leave to set in the fridge.

When set, turn out on to a large plate and decorate with lemon wedges.

· broccoli and almond lasagne ·

serves 4–6

A delightful, filling dish. To save time, use no-pre-cook lasagne
and cook according to instructions.

---

1 lb (450 g) broccoli florets
1 large onion
2 cloves garlic
3 tablespoons unrefined, cold-pressed olive oil
2 14 oz (392 g) tins of tomatoes
1 teaspoon dried oregano
1 teaspoon dried marjoram
freshly ground black pepper
sea salt
4 oz (112 g) shelled almonds, chopped
2 oz (56 g) ground almonds
8 oz (225 g) wholewheat no-pre-cook lasagne
10 fl oz (300 ml) cheese sauce (see p. 251)
2 oz (56 g) grated Parmesan

Break the broccoli into small pieces, chop the onion finely
and crush the garlic.

Heat the oil in a medium saucepan. Put in the onion
and garlic, cover and gently cook until soft.

Add the broccoli and tomatoes (breaking the latter up
with a wooden spoon). Cover and cook on medium heat until
the broccoli is just tender, then add the herbs and seasoning
to taste.

Remove from the heat and add the chopped and ground
almonds. Preheat the oven to 180°C (350°F, Mark 4).

Cook the lasagne in a large pan of lightly salted boiling
water, for about 10 to 12 minutes, according to the instructions, until it is just tender. Add one sheet at a time to
prevent sticking. When ready, drain, rinse and drain again
and spread the lasagne out on to a damp cloth to prevent
sticking.

Put one layer of lasagne along the bottom of a lightly-
greased 7 × 11 in (18 × 28 cm), 2 in (5 cm) deep, ovenproof

dish. Put in about a third of the broccoli mixture, then quickly make the cheese sauce.

Cover the first layer of broccoli with half the cheese sauce. Add another layer of lasagne, another third of the broccoli mixture, then the remaining cheese sauce, and finish with the final layer of lasagne, the rest of the broccoli and sprinkle the Parmesan on top. Bake in the oven for 20–25 minutes until the Parmesan looks golden brown and the cheese is bubbling.

For extra calcium
Serve with watercress or Chinese leaf, watercress and peach salads (see pp. 25, 97).

· *chickpea and cheese bake* ·
serves 4–6
My favourite vegetarian dish and always a great success at pot-luck events.

---

8 oz (225 g) chickpeas

4 oz (112 g) freshly-made wholemeal breadcrumbs

1 $15\frac{1}{2}$ oz (434 g) tin unsweetened pineapple pieces (including juice)

5 tablespoons unsweetened pineapple juice

1 small onion

4 sticks celery

4 tablespoons freshly chopped parsley

2 free-range eggs, beaten

5 tablespoons unrefined, cold-pressed olive oil

1 teaspoon tamari (soy sauce)

a few dashes chilli sauce

few pinches cayenne pepper

$\frac{1}{2}$ teaspoon paprika

6 oz (168 g) Cheddar cheese, grated

Garnish
sprigs of parsley

Soak the chickpeas overnight.

Drain. Cover with fresh boiling water, return to the boil and fast-boil, uncovered, for at least 10 minutes. Cover and simmer for a further 50–80 minutes, until just soft. (If using a pressure cooker, cover with fresh water, bring to the boil and simmer for 25–30 minutes.) Drain.

Put the chickpeas in a food processor and grind coarsely. Preheat the oven to 190°C (375°F, Mark 5). Lightly grease a 2 lb (900 g) bread tin.

Combine the breadcrumbs, pineapple pieces (with juice) and pineapple juice in a large mixing bowl and leave to soak while you prepare the vegetables.

Dice the onion finely, thinly slice the celery and finely chop the parsley.

Add the chickpeas, the vegetables and all the other ingredients to the breadcrumb mixture and mix well in. Spread the mixture evenly into the bread tin and level the surface.

Bake in the middle of the oven for 45–55 minutes or until golden brown. Serve hot or cold, and garnish with sprigs of parsley.

For extra calcium

If you want a hot meal, serve with steamed kale or broccoli. A simple green salad goes well or better still, watercress or Chinese leaf, watercress and peach salads (see pp. 25, 97).

· *spicy prawns with coconut* ·
serves 4

A hot dish, tempered by the mild, creamy coconut. Serve on a bed of rice, with other spicy dishes. You will find creamed coconut in some supermarkets, and in Asian or Greek grocers.

---

1 lb (450 g) frozen cooked peeled prawns (defrost if frozen)
3 oz (84 g) creamed coconut
15 fl oz (450 ml) boiling water
1 large onion

4 cloves garlic •
1 green chilli
1 in (2.5 cm) piece of fresh ginger
3 tablespoons cold-pressed sunflower oil
1 teaspoon ground coriander
2 teaspoons ground cumin
pinch cinnamon
1 teaspoon ground turmeric
1 teaspoon chilli powder
2 tablespoons tomato purée
freshly ground black pepper

Garnish
wedges of fresh lemon

Make sure the prawns are properly defrosted, if using them from frozen.

Make the coconut milk by grating the creamed coconut into a jug. Add the boiling water and stir until all the coconut has dissolved.

Finely chop the onion and crush the garlic. Top and tail the chilli, slit it down the side and remove the seeds, then slice finely. Peel and grate the ginger.

Heat the oil on medium heat in a large saucepan or heavy-bottomed pan, add the onion, garlic and chilli, cover and cook until soft, then add the ginger and spices and stir in well. Cover and cook for about a minute. Stir in the tomato purée and the coconut milk. Bring to the boil, stirring all the time. Cover and simmer gently for five minutes.

Stir in the prawns, heat through for several minutes making sure they are coated with sauce, then season with pepper. Garnish with lemon wedges and serve immediately with coconut rice (see p. 113).

For extra calcium
Serve with spicy okra and yoghurt (see p. 182).

· tofu burgers ·

makes about 8

These burgers are perfect for anyone who cannot eat dairy produce. They are very popular with children and some previously sceptical adults like them too. If you buy the tofu loose, you will need about two-thirds the amount. You can find oatbran and oatgerm in health shops.

---

1 lb (450 g) firm tofu (beancurd), about 2 packets including water

2 teaspoons tamari (soy sauce)

1 small onion

2 sticks celery

1 clove garlic

1 tablespoon unrefined, cold-pressed sunflower oil

2 tablespoons freshly chopped parsley

1 tablespoon tomato purée

2 oz (56 g) shelled almonds, ground

1 teaspoon freshly squeezed lemon juice

2 oz (56 g) freshly made wholemeal breadcrumbs

2 oz (56 g) oatbran and oatgerm

For coating
½ to 1 oz (14–28 g) soya flour

For shallow-frying
unrefined, cold-pressed sunflower oil

For the topping
1 oz (28 g) toasted sesame seeds (see p. 43)

Preheat the oven to 180°C (350°F, Mark 4) and toast the sesame seeds.

Drain the water off the tofu. Put in a bowl, mash with a fork and add the tamari.

Finely chop the onion and celery and crush the garlic. Heat the oil in a frying pan, add the onions, celery and garlic, cover and cook until soft.

Finely chop the parsley, then add the onion, celery, garlic, parsley, tomato purée, ground almonds, lemon juice, breadcrumbs, oatbran and oatgerm to the tofu, making sure all the ingredients are mixed well in.

Shape into burgers or croquettes, about $1\frac{1}{2}$ in (3.8 cm) in diameter. The mixture should be quite moist and will stick together surprisingly easily. (If you are worried about the burgers falling apart, you can dip them in beaten egg.) Spread the soya flour on a clean surface and coat the burgers with flour on both sides.

Put the oil in a heavy-based pan, to a depth of about $\frac{1}{4}$ in (6 mm). Get it hot on medium heat and shallow-fry the burgers until they are golden brown on both sides. (The first one should sizzle when the fat is hot enough.) Remove with a slotted spoon and drain on kitchen paper. Sprinkle with toasted sesame seeds and serve hot in wholemeal buns or, if you have made croquettes, serve with tomato sauce (see p. 249).

For extra calcium
Serve with watercress or Chinese leaf, watercress and peach salads (see pp. 25, 97) or hot vegetables such as steamed broccoli or spring greens.

· stir-fry tofu with vegetables ·
serves 4

A very simple low-fat meal that is quick to make after the initial preparation. Make sure you dry the beancurd thoroughly, otherwise it will disintegrate. If you buy it loose, you will need about two-thirds the amount. Tofu, sesame oil and arrowroot can be found in health shops or Chinese supermarkets.

---

1 lb (450 g) firm tofu (beancurd), about 2 packets including water

3 tablespoons unrefined, cold-pressed sunflower oil

6 spring onions

2 sticks celery

4 oz (112 g) Chinese leaf

4 oz (112 g) spinach

4 oz (112 g) broccoli florets
2 carrots
2 oz (56 g) alfalfa sprouts
2 cloves garlic
1 teaspoon freshly grated ginger
1 green chilli
freshly ground black pepper

For the sauce
1 teaspoon arrowroot
1 tablespoon dry sherry
2 tablespoons tamari (soy sauce)
5 fl oz (150 ml) vegetable stock
2 teaspoons unrefined, cold-pressed sesame oil

Drain the tofu, rinse and cut into ½ in (1.3 cm) cubes. Place on kitchen paper and blot dry.

Heat 2 tablespoons of oil in a wok or large frying pan on moderate heat. Add the tofu and stir-fry until lightly browned on both sides. Remove with a slotted spoon and drain on kitchen paper.

Prepare the sauce before you cut the vegetables. Put the arrowroot in a small bowl and blend with a little water until you have a thinnish cream. Mix in the sherry and tamari. Add the vegetable stock and the sesame oil and mix in well.

Now prepare the vegetables (working as quickly as possible to prevent loss of vitamins).

Slice the spring onions diagonally, including the green part, into 1 in (2.5 cm) lengths, thinly slice the celery diagonally, then cut the Chinese leaf into ½ in (1.3 cm) widths and chop coarsely. Remove the stalks from the spinach, rinse, pat dry with kitchen paper or dry in a salad-spinner, and chop coarsely. If there are any broccoli stalks, cut them off and cut diagonally into thin strips.

Blanch the broccoli by plunging it in boiling water and cooking for 1 minute. Drain, retaining the cooking water for vegetable stock.

Trim the tops and bases off the carrots, keeping them for

use in vegetable stock. Cut the carrots down the centre, lengthways. Cut again lengthways, then into thin matchstick-width strips about 1 in (2.5 cm) long. Separate the alfalfa sprouts as much as possible, crush the garlic, peel and grate the ginger and top and tail the chilli, slitting it down the side, removing the seeds and slicing finely. Now you are ready to start cooking the vegetables.

Add 1 tablespoon of oil to the wok, get it hot on moderate heat, add the garlic, chilli and ginger and stir-fry for 1 minute. Add the spring onions, celery and Chinese leaf and stir-fry for another minute, then add the spinach, broccoli, alfalfa and carrot and stir-fry for 1 minute.

Add the sauce and stir-fry the vegetables on high heat until the sauce thickens, then return the tofu to the pan and heat through thoroughly. Season with pepper if required and serve immediately, with brown rice, or wholewheat or spinach noodles.

· *carob cake* ·

Carob has a distinctive flavour, yet it contains none of the nasties of chocolate or cocoa. A moist, filling cake, the last morsels of which have to be fought over in our house! You can buy carob bars and apple and pear spread in health shops.

---

6 oz (168 g) unsalted butter or polyunsaturated margarine

6 oz (168 g) raw muscovado sugar

4 free-range eggs, separated

$\frac{1}{2}$ teaspoon natural almond essence

2 oz (56 g) carob powder

2 teaspoons baking powder

2 oz (56 g) soya flour

2 oz (56 g) shelled almonds, ground

Filling

4 oz (112 g) dried pitted dates

1 tablespoon apple and pear spread

For the topping
2 2½ oz (70 g) carob bars (with no added sugar)
2 tablespoons water
flaked almonds to decorate

Preheat the oven to 190°C (375°F, Mark 5) and lightly grease an 8 in (20 cm) round cake tin.

Cream together the butter or margarine and sugar until light and fluffy, beat in the egg yolks one at a time, then add the almond essence.

Sift the carob powder into a separate bowl and mix in the baking powder, soya flour and ground almonds.

In yet another bowl, whisk the egg whites until stiff. Fold the egg whites and the dry mixture alternately into the butter and sugar. Mix in well.

Spoon the mixture into the prepared cake tin and spread evenly. Bake in the middle of the oven for 30–35 minutes or until the cake is firm to the touch and a skewer comes out clean. Turn on to a wire rack to cool.

For the filling

Put the dates in a pan and only just cover with water. Gently cook them for 10–15 minutes or until soft. Watch that they do not burn as the water becomes absorbed.

Remove from the heat and mash them into a purée with a fork. Mix in the apple and pear spread while the dates are still warm, and leave to cool. When ready, cut the cake in half and spread the date mixture over the bottom half. Put the top in place.

For the topping

Break the carob bars on to a heat-resistant plate or flat dish. Place the plate over a pan of boiling water on a gentle heat and melt them, stirring in the water to make a smooth paste. Keep stirring to ensure that the carob does not curdle.

Spread evenly over the top of the cake, before the carob has time to dry out and thicken. Decorate with flaked almonds.

· *almond and apricot slices* ·

makes about 12 slices

Almonds and apricots seem to have a natural affinity. Used here together, they make these simple sugar-free slices wonderfully moist.

---

8 oz (225 g) unsulphured dried apricots

2 free-range eggs

2 tablespoons concentrated apple juice

1 teaspoon natural vanilla essence

4 oz (112 g) shelled almonds, ground

4 oz (112 g) flaked almonds

For the crust

wholemeal shortcrust pastry made with 6 oz (168 g) flour
(see p. 253)

Put the apricots in a pan. Just cover with water and cook for 20–30 minutes until soft.

Preheat the oven to 200°C (400°F, Mark 6). Lightly grease a 9 × 7 in (23 × 18 cm) baking sheet. Roll the pastry out thinly to fit the baking sheet. Press well in and prick all over with a fork. Bake blind for 5 minutes to set it. Reduce the oven heat to 190°C (375°F, Mark 5).

Put the apricots (and any liquid left) in a food processor and purée until smooth. Spread over the base of the baking sheet.

Beat the eggs in a bowl, add the concentrated apple juice, vanilla essence, the ground and flaked almonds and mix in well. Spread the mixture over the apricots.

Bake in the middle of the oven for 15–20 minutes until golden. Allow to cool before cutting into slices. Store in an airtight container or freeze.

6
·
MAGNESIUM
·

Magnesium is the second most abundant mineral inside cells after potassium. 70 per cent is found in the bones and teeth and the rest is found in body cells. It is involved in many metabolic processes including the maintenance of a correct distribution of sodium, potassium and calcium across cell membranes.

Magnesium, inside the body cells, works with calcium outside, to ensure the steady, smooth conduction of nerve impulses. If the balance of these two minerals is upset, symptoms may occur.

Certain nutrients, notably vitamin D and phosphorus, increase the body's requirements for magnesium in order to maintain a balance with calcium; magnesium itself is essential for the effective utilization of vitamins B_1 and B_6.

It is possible that phytates, found especially in raw bran, inhibit the absorption of magnesium, but bacteria in the colon probably break down the fibre, depending which kind it is, to release magnesium for absorption.

Signs of deficiency

Because magnesium is involved in so many enzymic processes, a deficiency may have widespread metabolic consequences. This is usually manifested in nervous conditions including hyperactivity, apathy, nausea, convulsions, weakness and tiredness, muscle cramps, uncontrollably flickering eyes, tremors and jerks and lack of muscular co-ordination. In extreme cases, magnesium deficiency may cause tetany – a continuous cramp in the hands and feet.

THOSE MOST AT RISK OF DEFICIENCY

- Those who eat a diet high in processed and refined foods.

- Diabetics, because much magnesium is lost through the large volumes of urine passed.

- Chronic alcoholics. Alcohol acts as a diuretic, causing vast quantities of magnesium to be lost in the urine.

- Bottle-fed babies. Formula milk and fresh cow's milk contain a high proportion of phosphorus, which increases the babies' need for magnesium.

- Those taking diuretics which cause magnesium depletion through losses in the urine.

- Breast-feeding women

Requirements may also increase if you have a high protein, calcium or Vitamin D intake.

Therapeutic uses

It is only fairly recently that magnesium deficiency has been recognized as a possible contributing factor to a variety of conditions. Some of the conditions that have been helped by magnesium are:

- Heart disease. Magnesium has been used extensively in the treatment of heart attacks and irregularities of the heart such as tachycardia. In these cases, magnesium deficiency causes the coronary arteries to go into spasm and the heart beats irregularly because it is in a state of increased excitability.

- High blood pressure. Magnesium has been used successfully to lower the blood pressure of those suffering from hypertension, caused by hardening of the arteries. It is possible that the diuretics used to treat hypertension may have caused a magnesium deficiency because of the great losses of magnesium in the urine.

● Psychiatric problems. Because of its calming effect on the nervous system, magnesium has been used as a natural tranquilliser to help alleviate insomnia, depression, anorexia, apathy, childhood hyperactivity and anxiety.

● Premenstrual syndrome. Magnesium has helped many women suffering from premenstrual tension who have been found to have a low level of it in their red blood cells. This deficiency seems to affect mental function, the control of blood sugar levels and energy, and also the metabolism of some hormones.

● Osteoporosis. This is a condition where calcium is removed from the bones, causing them to become brittle and to fracture easily. Extra magnesium has been shown to help in some cases of osteoporosis where it is thought deficiency has contributed to the condition. The magnesium helps to restore the balance with calcium and assists the absorption of calcium from food and its retention in the body.

● Kidney stones. Supplements of magnesium and vitamin B_6 have been found to prevent the formation of urinary oxalate stones, which are usually formed when there is excess oxalic acid in the urine and a magnesium deficiency has developed.

Sources of magnesium

Food	Mg per 100 g	Food	Mg per 100 g
Cocoa powder	520	Walnuts	130
Wheat bran	520	Wholemeal flour	120
Brazil nuts	410	Dried peas	116
Winkles, boiled	360	Rye	115*
Sesame seeds	347	Brown rice	110
Coriander seeds	330	Oatmeal	110
Wheatgerm	270	Shrimps, boiled	110
Cashew nuts	267	Plain chocolate	100
Soya beans	265	Dried figs	92
Almonds	260	Rye flour	92
Blackstrap molasses	258*	Pot barley	91
Caraway seeds	258	Desiccated coconut	90
Soy flour	240	Bamboo shoots, canned	88
Brewer's yeast	231*	Spinach	88
Haricot beans	180	Lentils	77
Marmite (yeast extract)	180	Wholemeal bread	76
Peanut butter	180	Tomato purée	66
Peanuts	180	Dried apricots	65
Red kidney beans	180	Okra	60
Millet	170**	Dried dates	59
Mung beans	170	Anchovies, canned in oil, fish only	56
Oats	169*	Hazelnuts	56
Butter beans	164	Dried peaches	54
Chickpeas	160	Blackeye beans	53
Chinese leaves	160	Macaroni	53
Wheat	160*	Coconut	52
Whelks, boiled	160	Sardines in oil, fish only	52
Pistachio nuts	158*	Cockles, boiled	51
Pecan nuts	142*	Parmesan cheese	50
Bulgur wheat	140	Buckwheat	48
Red pigeon peas	130	Crab, boiled	48
Split peas	130	Kipper, baked	48

Food	Mg per 100 g	Food	Mg per 100 g
Noodles	47	Bananas	42
Shrimps, frozen, shell removed	47	Oysters	42
Sprats, fried	46	Prawns, boiled	42
Sweetcorn, on the cob	46	Raisins	42

· hannah's hummus ·

serves 4

Hummus is a perfect party dip. You can serve it with spicy tortilla chips, milder corn chips or simple crudités such as sticks of carrot, celery or green pepper. Add more garlic, olive oil and lemon juice to taste.

---

8 oz (225 g) chickpeas
4–6 fl oz (120–180 ml) cooking water
2 cloves garlic
2 tablespoons unrefined, cold-pressed olive oil
freshly squeezed juice of 1–2 lemons
5 oz (140 g) tahini (sesame spread)

Garnish
paprika
freshly chopped parsley

Soak the chickpeas overnight.

Drain. Cover with fresh boiling water. Return to the boil and fast-boil, uncovered, for 10 minutes. Cover and simmer gently for a further 50–80 minutes, until soft but crunchy. (If you are using a pressure cooker, bring to the boil and simmer for 25–30 minutes.) Drain, keeping the cooking water to use in the dip.

Place the chickpeas in a blender with the garlic. Purée with enough cooking water to soften. (Do not make it too runny at this stage; you can always add more liquid later.)

42

Gradually add the olive oil, lemon juice and tahini and work into a smooth creamy paste.

Adjust the seasoning to taste, adding more lemon juice or garlic as necessary. Add more cooking liquid if it is too thick. Spoon into a serving bowl or individual ramekins, cover and chill.

Just before serving, sprinkle with paprika and garnish with freshly chopped parsley.

For extra magnesium
Serve with hot wholemeal pitta bread.

· sesame oatcakes ·
makes about 20

Home-made oatcakes make ideal snacks, especially when spread with vegetable, meat or fish paté, or topped with cheese.

---

2 oz (56 g) sesame seeds
8 oz (225 g) fine or medium oatmeal
$\frac{1}{4}$ teaspoon sea salt
good pinch of baking powder
$1\frac{1}{4}$ oz (35 g) unsalted butter or polyunsaturated margarine
boiling water to mix (about 4–5 tablespoons)
wholemeal flour to spread on the work surface

Preheat the oven to 190°C (375°F, Mark 5).

To toast the sesame seeds, spread them on a baking sheet and put in the oven for 20 minutes, shaking them round occasionally. Remove from the oven and mix together the sesame seeds, oatmeal, salt and baking powder in a large bowl. When the baking sheet has cooled down, grease it lightly.

Melt the butter or margarine in a small saucepan over a gentle heat and stir into the oatmeal mix. Gradually add enough boiling water to make a stiff dough, but do not add so much that it becomes sticky. Turn the dough out on to a clean, lightly floured work surface and gently knead until smooth.

Roll out very thinly and cut into a large rectangle. Cut into adjoining triangles, pick up carefully with a palette knife or slice and place on the baking sheet. Bake in the middle of the oven for 10–15 minutes. Leave to cool slightly, then transfer to a wire rack. Store in an airtight container.

· *chinese leaf and cashew salad* ·

serves 4

The crunchy texture of Chinese leaf makes it a perfect salad vegetable, and it has more flavour than most lettuces. Buy a tightly packed, rather than loose-leafed one. This light salad goes well with heavy pasta dishes, or with fish.

---

3 tablespoons honey and mint dressing (see p. 239)
12 oz (336 g) Chinese leaf
4 oz (112 g) shelled cashew nuts
2 oranges

Make the dressing first to minimize loss of vitamins and minerals from the salad by exposure to light and oxygen.

Cut the Chinese leaf into slices about $\frac{1}{4}$ in (6 mm) thick (it should fall away quite simply into shreds) and put in a large salad bowl. Chop the cashews into large pieces and mix in.

Peel the oranges over the bowl, to catch the juice, break into segments and add to the salad. If you remove the pith, cut it into tiny pieces and mix in. Toss the salad in the dressing until it is thoroughly coated. Serve immediately.

· *tropical rice salad* ·

serves 4

There is an interesting blend of sweet and savoury in this substantial salad. It goes well with hot, spicy dishes.

2 oz (56 g) creamed coconut
1 pt (600 ml) boiling water
5 oz (140 g) long-grain brown rice
1 teaspoon turmeric
3 fl oz (90 ml) tropical dressing (see p. 248)
3 oz (84 g) shelled cashew nut pieces
3 oz (84 g) sunflower seeds
2 oz (56 g) sultanas
1 large fresh green chilli
2 tablespoons freshly chopped coriander leaves
1 banana
$\frac{1}{4}$ teaspoon paprika
sea salt
freshly ground black pepper

To make coconut milk, grate the coconut into a jug and pour in the boiling water. Stir until the coconut is completely dissolved. Put the rice in a large saucepan with the turmeric. Add the coconut milk, bring to the boil, cover and simmer for 30–40 minutes until the rice is soft and all the water has been absorbed. Stir occasionally to prevent sticking. Add more water if necessary. Now make the dressing.

Leave the rice to cool then add the cashews, sunflower seeds and sultanas. Mix in well. (Once the rice cools, it will become quite dry, because of the coconut, but this doesn't matter because you will be adding a moist dressing.)

Top and tail the chilli, slit the side and remove the seeds. (If you like your salad hot, leave them in.) Finely chop the chilli and the coriander leaves and mix them in with the salad. Thinly slice the bananas and mix in.

Add the paprika and season with salt and pepper. Mix the dressing well in with the salad. Serve immediately.

· *spicy chickpeas* ·
serves 4

Serve this on a bed of brown rice to make a complete protein meal, or with potatoes and other vegetables. Alternatively, use as one of several curried dishes, and cool down with refreshing yoghurt and cucumber dip (see p. 121).

---

12 oz (336 g) chickpeas
1 large onion
2 fresh green chillies
2 cloves garlic
1 teaspoon fresh root ginger, peeled and grated
2 tablespoons unrefined, cold-pressed sunflower oil
2 teaspoons ground cumin
1 teaspoon ground coriander
$\frac{1}{2}$ teaspoon ground turmeric
2 tablespoons tomato purée
1 14 oz (392 g) tin tomatoes
10 fl oz (300 ml) reserved cooking liquid
8 oz (225 g) spinach
1 teaspoon garam masala
sea salt
freshly ground black pepper

Garnish
1 tablespoon freshly chopped coriander leaves

Soak the chickpeas overnight.

Drain. Cover with boiling water. Return to the boil and fast-boil, uncovered, for 10 minutes. Cover and simmer for a further 50–80 minutes until just soft. (If using a pressure cooker, bring to the boil and simmer for 25–30 minutes.) Drain and retain the liquid.

Chop the onion finely. Top and tail the chillies, slit them down the side, remove the seeds and slice finely. Crush the garlic, and peel and grate the ginger.

Heat the oil in a heavy-based pan. Put in the onion, chillies, garlic and ginger, cover and cook gently until soft. Add the spices, cooking gently for a minute or two while stirring. Add the tomato purée, the tomatoes (breaking them up with a wooden spoon) and the chickpeas, cover, bring to the boil and simmer gently for 5 minutes. Then add the reserved cooking water, bring to the boil and simmer gently for 20 minutes, stirring occasionally. If the mixture starts to stick, add a little more liquid.

Wash the spinach, remove the stalks and chop coarsely. Add to the pan and cook for a further 5 minutes. Stir in the garam masala and season with salt and pepper.

Chop the coriander leaves and sprinkle them over the chickpeas. Serve immediately.

For extra magnesium
Serve with brown rice or coconut rice (see pp. 113) and spicy okra with yoghurt (see p. 182).

· *soya bean croquettes* ·
Makes about 12

A tasty way to serve beans is to use them to make croquettes, served with a moist sauce. These croquettes go well with a grain such as rice or millet, or with salads or hot vegetables.

---

4 oz (112 g) soya beans
1 oz (28 g) Cheddar cheese, grated
1 oz (28 g) shelled Brazil nuts, chopped finely
1 oz (28 g) wheatgerm
dash tamari (soy sauce)
sea salt
freshly ground black pepper
2 tablespoons tomato purée
½ teaspoon dried oregano or 1 teaspoon freshly chopped
  oregano
1 clove garlic, crushed
1 tablespoon freshly chopped parsley

For coating
1 free-range egg, beaten
1 oz (28 g) sesame seeds, toasted

For shallow-frying
unrefined, cold-pressed sunflower oil

To serve
tomato sauce (see p. 249)

Cover the beans with boiling water, return to the boil and fast-boil uncovered for 1 hour. Cover and continue to simmer for 1 more hour, until soft. (If using a pressure cooker, cover with water, bring to the boil and simmer for 40–45 minutes.) Drain.

Preheat the oven to 190°C (375°F, Mark 5). To toast the sesame seeds, spread them on a baking sheet and put in the oven for 20 minutes, shaking them around once or twice. If you are going to cook the croquettes in the oven, leave it on the same temperature and lightly grease a large baking sheet.

Mash the soya beans or put in a food processor and grind to a thick purée. Mix with all the other ingredients.

Shape into balls, about 1½ in (3.8 cm) in diameter. Coat with the beaten egg, spread the sesame seeds out on a clean surface and roll the balls in them until covered.

Put the oil in a heavy-based pan, to a depth of ¼ in (6 mm), on a moderate heat. When the oil is hot (the first croquette should sizzle), shallow-fry the croquettes for 4–5 minutes, turning regularly, until golden brown. Drain on kitchen paper and serve hot with tomato sauce.

If cooking in the oven, place on the baking sheet, cover with foil and bake for 20 minutes.

For extra magnesium
Serve with savoury millet or tropical rice salad (see below and p. 44) and steamed spinach or stir-fried Chinese leaf.

· *savoury millet* ·
serves 4

Millet is a much underestimated grain, but it has an interesting texture and blandish flavour that can be enhanced in many different ways. You can buy it in health shops. Serve this dish hot as a main course, with salads or vegetables, or as an accompaniment to spicy dishes.

---

1 small onion
2 cloves garlic

1 tablespoon unrefined, cold-pressed olive oil
8 oz (225 g) millet
1 pt (600 ml) boiling water
5 oz (140 g) Cheddar cheese, grated
2 oz (56 g) shelled walnuts, chopped into large pieces
3 oz (84 g) sultanas
1 tablespoon freshly chopped parsley
freshly ground black pepper

Finely chop the onion and crush the garlic. Heat the oil in a saucepan and gently fry them until soft.

Add the millet and stir-fry it for a minute. Pour in the boiling water, return to the boil, cover and simmer gently for 15–20 minutes until the millet has a light and fluffy texture and all the water has been absorbed. It may cook very quickly so stir it occasionally to prevent burning and, if necessary, add more water.

Remove from the heat and stir in the grated cheese until it has all melted, then mix in the walnuts, sultanas and parsley. Season to taste.

If serving hot, return to the heat for a short time, stirring quickly to prevent burning. Serve immediately.

For extra magnesium
Serve with Chinese leaf and cashew salad (see p. 44) or with spicy chickpeas (see p. 45).

· *dried fruit salad* ·
serves 4

A rich, naturally sweet fruit salad that you can make all year round. It is very easy to make and is popular with children (without the rum!). Serve with yoghurt for contrasting flavour.

10 fl oz (300 ml) unsweetened orange juice
2 tablespoons rum, preferably dark brown
6 cloves

pinch ground cinnamon
pinch ground mixed spice
3 oz (84 g) dried figs
3 oz (84 g) unsulphured dried apricots
2 oz (56 g) dried dates
1 banana
2 oz (56 g) mixed brazil nuts, hazelnuts or cashew nuts,
chopped

Mix together the orange juice, rum, cloves, cinnamon and mixed spice in a large bowl.

Add the figs, apricots and dates, mix in well to make sure they are thoroughly covered with the juice. Cover and leave to soak overnight.

Remove the cloves and add more juice if required. Just before serving, thinly slice the banana and mix in well. Put the fruit mixture into individual bowls and sprinkle with nuts. Serve immediately.

7

·

IRON

·

The main function of iron is to carry oxygen from the lungs to every cell of the body, in the form of haemoglobin, the red pigment of the blood, and as myoglobin, the pigment of muscle. It is also a vital component of many of the body's enzyme systems.

The body of an adult contains 3–4 grams of iron, more than half of which is in the form of haemoglobin. The rest is stored in the liver, spleen and bone marrow, and in the muscles as myoglobin.

Iron is extremely hard to absorb. Only about 10 per cent of iron from foods of animal origin (haem iron) is absorbed, and about 5 per cent of iron found in plant foods (non-haem iron). However, vitamin C enhances the absorption of iron. So a drink of fresh orange juice, taken with an egg for breakfast, will considerably increase the amount of iron available from the egg.

Many substances reduce the absorption of iron. For example, foods rich in phytates, such as raw bran and soya products, can inhibit the absorption of iron. Excessive supplementation of zinc and copper have the same effect. Foods high in phosphates immobilize vegetarian (non-haem) iron, making it unavailable to the body. Tannin, found in tea and coffee, reduces iron absorption, especially if these drinks are taken with meals.

Signs of deficiency

According to the World Health Organization, iron is the most widely deficient mineral in the world. This is partly because in developing countries, much of the iron that people eat is rendered unabsorbable, because it is bound in the intestine by phytic acid (phytates).

Iron deficiency can cause many symptoms, most of which are linked to anaemia.

Symptoms of anaemia include: tiredness, fatigue, lack of stamina, breathlessness and pallor. Sometimes, however, iron deficiency exists without any blood changes or signs of anaemia.

In children, poor appetite, poor growth and decreased resistance to infection are common. Iron deficiency also causes impaired learning ability and behavioural and learning problems. This may be because iron deficiency increases children's ability to absorb toxic metals such as lead and cadmium that are increasingly implicated in behavioural and learning problems.

THOSE MOST AT RISK OF DEFICIENCY

Women of child-bearing age are at greatest risk of iron deficiency because of menstrual blood loss. Some people of both sexes are susceptible to iron deficiency because they lose blood on a long-term basis, for example, through haemorrhoids that bleed occasionally, or through regular use of aspirin that can cause blood loss from the stomach. Any blood lost has to be replaced from the body's store of iron. If the intake from food is not sufficient, this store becomes depleted and illness may occur. Those most at risk of iron deficiency include:

- Vegetarians. They may be at risk of iron deficiency because of its poor absorption from non-meat foods. However, provided they eat plenty of vitamin C, most vegetarians should be able to compensate for this.

- Children.
- Women of child-bearing age, especially those with heavy periods or who have had repeated pregnancies.
- Pregnant and breast-feeding women.
- Anyone with a poor diet such as: the elderly, those from low socio-economic groups and fanatical slimmers.

Others who may be at risk are those with malabsorption problems, those who are on exclusion diets for food allergy and those with very little gastric acid, following the removal of part of their stomach.

Therapeutic uses

Extra iron is most often needed in pregnancy and many pregnant women are routinely prescribed iron supplements. These should be taken with caution since they inhibit the absorption of zinc and sometimes cause constipation and gut upsets.

Women considering pregnancy would be better advised to eat an iron-rich diet with plenty of vitamin C to promote iron absorption and to avoid tea and coffee.

Sources of iron

Food	Mg per 100 g	Food	Mg per 100 g
Dulse	150.0a	Winkles, boiled	15.0
Curry powder	29.6	Pistachio nuts	14.0
Cockles, boiled	26.0b	Alfalfa	12.9*
Pig's liver	21.0	Wheat bran	12.9
Black pudding, fried	20.0	Arame	12.0c
Dried yeast	20.0	Chinese mushrooms, dried	11.7
Pigeon, roast	19.4	Aduki beans	11.6**
Blackstrap molasses	16.1*	Pumpkin seeds	11.2*

Food	Mg per 100 g	Food	Mg per 100 g
Hare, stewed	10.8	Split peas	5.4
Chicken liver	9.5	Tofu, fried	5.2
Irish moss (carragheen)	8.9*	Tomato purée	5.1
Lamb's liver	8.7	Whitebait, fried	5.1
Malt extract	8.7*	Couscous	5.0
Wheatgerm	8.5	Pasta verdi	5.0d
Pheasant, roast	8.4	Pig's kidney	5.0
Soya beans	8.4	Red pigeon peas	5.0
Calf's liver	8.0	Bulgur wheat	4.9
Mung beans	8.0	Ox heart	4.9
Parsley	8.0	Pig's heart	4.8
Agar, dried	7.8	Dried peas	4.7
Sesame seeds	7.8	Goose, roast	4.6
Venison	7.8	Sardines, canned in tomato sauce	4.6
Partridge, roast	7.7	Soy sauce, dark, thick	4.4
Grouse, roast	7.6	Brazil nuts	4.2
Lentils	7.6	Broad beans	4.2
Lamb's kidney	7.4	Cornmeal, unsifted	4.2
Sunflower seeds	7.1*	Dried figs	4.2
Ox liver	7.0	Anchovies, canned in oil, fish only	4.1
Soya flour	6.9	Dried apricots	4.1
Dried peaches	6.8	Oatmeal	4.1
Millet	6.8*	Stoneground whole-wheat pasta	4.0e
Haricot beans	6.7	Wholemeal flour	3.9
Kidney beans	6.7	Cashew nuts	3.8
Blackeye beans	6.5	Desiccated coconut	3.6
Chickpeas	6.4	Lamb's heart	3.6
Whelks, boiled	6.2	Red chillies	3.6
Egg yolk	6.1	Sprats	3.2
Oysters	6.0	Almonds	3.1
Pot barley	6.0	Buckwheat	3.1*
Butter beans	5.9	Spinach	3.1
Mussels	5.8		
Ox kidney	5.7		

Food	Mg per 100 g	Food	Mg per 100 g
Peanut butter	3.0	Pecan nuts	2.4*
Peanuts	3.0	Vine leaves	2.3
Scallops	3.0	Bloater, grilled	2.2
Walnuts	3.0	Beef	2.1
Chinese leaves	2.9	Coconut	2.1
Dried prunes	2.9	Spaghetti	2.1
Sardines, canned in oil, fish only		Buckwheat	2.0
		Eggs	2.0
Endive	2.8	Globe artichoke	2.0
Wholemeal bread	2.7	Pilchards, canned in tomato sauce	2.0
Shrimps, frozen, shell removed	2.6	Vermicelli	2.0
Courgettes	2.4	Peas	1.9
Duck	2.4	Radishes	1.9
Hazelnuts	2.4		

Notes:

a and c Information taken from *Vegetables from the Sea* by Toruko and Seibin Arasaki.
b Can be up to 40 mg per 100 g.
d and e Information supplied by Pasta Foods Ltd.

· *three bean salad* ·
serves 4

You can use any beans for this salad, as long as you have contrasting colours to make it look attractive. It's best to cook the kidney and flageolet beans separately to avoid discoloration. Serve as one of a range of salads or, to make a complete protein, with a grain or pasta.

2 oz (56 g) red kidney beans
2 oz (56 g) flageolet beans
5 fl oz (150 ml) herb dressing (see p. 240)
4 oz (112 g) fresh French beans

Soak the kidney and flageolet beans overnight in separate bowls.

Drain, put them in separate pans and cover with boiling water (about double their volume). Return to the boil and fast-boil uncovered for at least 10 minutes. This is especially important for the kidney beans which have been found to contain toxins. Reduce the heat, cover and simmer for a further 30–40 minutes until tender.

(If using a pressure cooker, you will have to do the beans in two lots. Cover with water, bring to the boil and simmer for 15 minutes.) While they are cooking make the salad dressing.

Drain, put the beans together in a large salad bowl, mix in the herb dressing and leave to marinate.

Top and tail the French beans and cut into $\frac{1}{2}$ in (1.3 cm) lengths. Steam over a pan of boiling water for 3–4 minutes until soft but still crunchy. Drain, retaining the water for use elsewhere as vegetable stock. Add them to the bowl and mix in well, making sure all the beans are thoroughly coated in the dressing. Cover and refrigerate for 30 minutes to allow the dressing to soak in.

· courgette and butter bean soup ·

serves 4–6

A naturally creamy soup for summer or winter. It is popular with children, especially those who normally turn their noses up at vegetables.

---

6 oz (168 g) butter beans
1 lb (450 g) courgettes
1 medium onion
1 oz (28 g) unsalted butter or polyunsaturated margarine
$\frac{1}{4}$ teaspoon nutmeg
sea salt
freshly ground black pepper
2 tablespoons freshly chopped parsley

Soak the butter beans overnight.

Drain. Put in a large pan, cover with boiling water (about double their volume), return to the boil and fast-boil uncovered for 10 minutes. Reduce the heat, cover and simmer for a further 25–40 minutes or until soft. Drain, retaining the water for use in the soup. (If using a pressure cooker, cover with fresh water and simmer for 10–15 minutes until soft. Drain, keeping the water for use in the soup.)

Thinly slice the courgettes and finely chop the onion. Melt the butter or margarine in a large saucepan, add the courgettes and onion and stir to coat with the butter. Cover and cook for 5 minutes, but do not allow to go brown.

Add the butter beans, 15 fl oz (450 ml) of drained water and the nutmeg; season with salt and pepper. Cover, bring to the boil and simmer for 10 minutes until the courgettes are tender.

Chop the parsley and mix in, then transfer the soup to a liquidizer and blend until smooth. Return to the pan, heat through and serve immediately.

For extra iron
Serve with hot wholemeal garlic bread.

· aduki bean and dulse soup ·

serves 4

Dulse has a mild flavour so if you have never eaten sea vegetables, it is a good one to start off with. This a wholesome soup that makes a filling meal. Do not be put off by its appearance. Dulse and aduki beans are available in health shops.

3 oz (84 g) aduki beans
1 oz (28 g) dulse (about half a packet)
1 medium onion
4 oz (112 g) mushrooms
1 tablespoon unrefined, cold-pressed sunflower oil

2½ pt (1,500 ml) vegetable stock
2 tablespoons freshly chopped parsley
freshly squeezed juice of 2 lemons

Garnish
sprigs of fresh parsley

Soak the aduki beans overnight. Drain.

Remove any barnacles from the dulse then soak in 10 fl oz (300 ml) water for 5 minutes. Drain and retain the water for use in the soup. Chop the dulse finely.

Finely chop the onion. Wipe the mushrooms with damp kitchen paper and slice finely. Heat the oil in a large saucepan, put in the onion and mushrooms, cover and cook gently for 5 minutes.

Add the beans and the stock. Bring to the boil and boil vigorously uncovered for 10 minutes. (This is to get rid of any toxins in the beans.) Add the dulse, with its soaking water. Bring to the boil, cover and simmer gently for about 40–50 minutes, until the beans are soft. Add more water if necessary. In the last five minutes, mix in the parsley.

Just before serving, squeeze the lemon juice and add to the soup. Garnish with sprigs of fresh parsley.

For extra iron
Serve with wholemeal bread.

· *mussel chowder* ·
serves 4–6

A chowder is a traditional fish and potato stew from the Atlantic shores of the USA and France. It is so filling that you can eat it as a main meal, with hot garlic bread. Mussels are best eaten fresh on the day of purchase. They are somewhat time-consuming to prepare, but the effort is always worth it.

---

3 lbs or 3 pt (approx 1½ kg) fresh mussels
10 fl oz (300 ml) dry white wine

15 fl oz (450 ml) water
1 oz (28 g) unsalted butter
6 rashers unsmoked streaky bacon, derinded and chopped
2 cloves garlic
1 large onion
2 large leeks
2 sticks celery
1½ lb (675 g) potatoes
1 tablespoon wholemeal flour
2 bay leaves
1 bouquet garni
pinch ground mace
pinch ground allspice
pinch ground cinnamon
freshly ground black pepper
6 tablespoons freshly chopped parsley
15 fl oz (450 ml) skimmed milk
5 fl oz (150 ml) single cream (optional)

Garnish
fresh parsley and chives

Scrub the mussels under cold running water with a stiff brush. Scrape off any barnacles with a sharp knife and pull off any beards. Rinse them several times in running water. Tap each mussel sharply with a knife and discard any that remain open – these are dead. Discard any broken ones.

Bring the wine and water to the boil in a large saucepan. Add the mussels, cover, return to the boil and simmer for 5 minutes, until the shells have opened. Drain and reserve the liquid for later. Discard any mussels that have not opened and remove the rest from their shells.

Dry the pan with kitchen paper and heat the butter. Cover and cook the bacon gently for a few minutes. Crush the garlic and finely slice the onion, leeks and celery. Add the garlic and onion, cover, cook gently for a few minutes, then add the leeks and celery, cover and cook until soft.

Cut the potatoes into large cubes, add to the pan, cover

and cook for a further 5 minutes. Stir in the flour and cook for a minute or two, making sure it does not stick. Gradually add the reserved liquid and bring to the boil. Put in the bay leaves, bouquet garni and spices and season well with pepper. Cover and simmer for about 15 minutes until the potatoes are almost cooked.

Chop the parsley and add to the pan with the mussels and the milk. Simmer gently for 5 more minutes. Remove the bouquet garni.

Just before serving, add the cream if required and heat through. Check the seasoning. Serve in individual bowls and garnish with more chopped parsley and chives.

For extra iron
Serve with piping hot wholemeal garlic bread.

· spinach and lentil curry ·

serves 4

Quick and easy to make, this curry goes well with brown rice or potatoes, or as one of a range of curried dishes, served with yoghurt sauce (see p. 250). If you prefer contrasting colours, use red lentils. These cook much more quickly so make sure they do not stick.

---

8 oz (225 g) whole green lentils
2 cloves garlic
2 large onions
3 fresh green chillies
1 in (2.5 cm) piece of fresh root ginger
1½ lb (675 g) fresh spinach
3 tablespoons unrefined, cold-pressed sunflower oil
½ teaspoon whole cumin seeds
½ teaspoon turmeric
½ teaspoon ground coriander
½ teaspoon cayenne pepper
2 tablespoons freshly squeezed lemon juice
sea salt

freshly ground black pepper

Garnish
sprigs of fresh coriander
lemon wedges

Pick over the lentils and remove any grit. Put in a large saucepan, cover with boiling water (about twice their volume), return to the boil, cover and simmer for about 20 minutes until soft. Drain.

Crush the garlic and finely chop the onions. Top and tail the chillies, slit them down the side and remove the seeds (or leave them if you want a very hot dish). Chop finely. Peel and grate the ginger. Wash the spinach, remove the stalks and chop coarsely.

Heat the oil on medium heat in a heavy-based pan, add the cumin seeds and cook for a few seconds. Add the garlic, onions, chillies and ginger, cover and cook until soft. Add the spinach, stirring regularly, until it has softened slightly, then add the turmeric, coriander, cayenne pepper, lemon juice and lentils, cover and cook for a further 10 minutes. There should be enough residual water to prevent sticking, but stir regularly to ensure this and add a touch more water if necessary. However, be careful not to make the dish too runny. Season with salt and pepper.

Transfer to a warmed serving dish and garnish with sprigs of fresh coriander. Serve immediately with wedges of lemon and yoghurt sauce (see p. 250).

For extra iron
Serve with brown rice.

· *liver with herbs* ·
serves 4
Pig's liver is an unbelievably cheap source of vitamins and minerals. It is slightly more bitter than lamb's liver and needs

a little more cooking. However, if you overcook it, it becomes tough. Ask your butcher to cut it up very thinly for you. Fresh herbs make all the difference to this dish. If they are unavailable, use half the quantity of dried herbs (not including the flour seasoning).

---

1 lb (450 g) pig's liver
2 tablespoons wholemeal flour
¼ teaspoon dried thyme
¼ teaspoon dried oregano
1 medium onion
4 oz (112 g) button mushrooms
3 medium courgettes
3 tablespoons unrefined, cold-pressed sunflower oil
5 fl oz (150 ml) red wine
5 fl oz (150 ml) vegetable stock
1 14 oz (392 g) tin tomatoes
2 tablespoons tomato purée
1 teaspoon freshly chopped thyme
1 bay leaf
1 tablespoon freshly chopped marjoram
sea salt
freshly ground black pepper

Garnish
3 tablespoons freshly chopped parsley

Rinse the liver thoroughly and pat dry with kitchen paper. Cut into very thin slices or into 1 in (2.5 cm) squares.

Put the flour in a small bowl and season with the dried herbs. Dip the liver into the seasoned flour so that it is coated all over.

Finely chop the onion. Wipe the mushrooms with damp kitchen paper, and finely slice the mushrooms and the courgettes.

Heat 2 tablespoons of the oil in a heavy-based pan and gently fry the liver for 2 minutes. Remove from the pan with a slotted spoon and keep warm. Scrape any residual flour off the base of the pan with a plastic slice. Add 1 tablespoon of oil to the pan and, when it is hot, add the onion. Cover and gently cook until transparent. Add the mushrooms and courgettes, cover and cook for another couple of minutes. Stir in the wine, the stock, the tinned tomatoes with their juice (breaking them up with the back of a spoon), the tomato purée, thyme and bay leaf. Cover, bring to the boil and simmer for 5 minutes.

Return the liver to the pan, cover and simmer gently for 25 minutes or until the liver is just tender. Just before the liver is ready, chop the marjoram, mix in and season with salt and pepper to taste. Remove the bay leaf before transferring to a warmed serving dish, sprinkle with freshly chopped parsley and serve immediately.

For extra iron
Serve with wholewheat pasta shells or noodles and steamed or stir-fried vegetables such as courgettes, broccoli, Chinese leaf, leeks or spring greens.

· *spicy mung bean croquettes* ·
makes 16–18 croquettes
These moist croquettes can be served with other curried dishes and a yoghurt sauce (see p. 250).

---

8 oz (225 g) mung beans

1 medium onion

2 cloves garlic

1 green chilli

1 medium green pepper

1 medium carrot

2 tablespoons unrefined, cold-pressed sunflower oil

$\frac{1}{2}$ teaspoon ground coriander

$\frac{1}{2}$ teaspoon ground cumin

$\frac{1}{2}$ teaspoon curry powder

$\frac{1}{4}$ teaspoon cayenne pepper

2 tablespoons tomato purée

2 tablespoons fresh parsley

1 teaspoon freshly squeezed lemon juice
sea salt
freshly ground black pepper

For coating
2 oz (56 g) fresh wholemeal breadcrumbs
2 oz (56 g) fine oatmeal
1–2 free-range eggs
2 oz (56 g) wholemeal flour

For shallow-frying
unrefined, cold-pressed sunflower oil

Garnish
lemons cut into wedges

Soak the mung beans overnight. Drain. Cover with boiling water, return to the boil and fast-boil for at least 10 minutes. Simmer for a further 20–35 minutes, until just soft. (If using a pressure cooker, bring to the boil and simmer for 10–15 minutes.) Drain.

Put the mung beans in a food processor and grind coarsely, or put them in a bowl and mash with a fork. Finely dice the onion, crush the garlic, top and tail the chilli, slitting the side and removing the seeds, and remove the top from the green pepper, taking out the seeds but not the core.

Finely chop the chilli, green pepper and carrot. (If you want, you can chop the vegetables in a food processor, as long as they don't become ground into a pulp.)

Heat the oil in a large frying pan on medium heat, put in the onion, garlic and chilli, cover and cook until soft. Add the green pepper and carrot, cover and cook for a few more minutes, then add the spices, tomato purée, parsley and lemon juice and mix in well. Season with salt and pepper to taste. Remove from the heat.

Make the breadcrumbs and combine with the oatmeal in a bowl. Beat the egg in a separate bowl.

Shape the mung bean mixture into balls, about 1½ in (3.8 cm) in diameter. Spread the flour out on a clean surface. Coat the croquettes in the flour, cover with egg and coat in the oatmeal mixture.

Put the oil in a large, heavy-based pan to a depth of
¼ in (6 mm). Get it really hot, on medium heat, and
shallow-fry the croquettes until golden brown on all sides.
Remove with a slotted spoon and drain on kitchen paper.
Serve hot with yoghurt sauce (see p. 250) and lemon
wedges.

To assist iron absorption
Serve with vegetables rich in vitamin C such as steamed
broccoli or cauliflower, or serve with watercress or Chinese
leaf, watercress and peach salads (see pp. 25, 97).

For extra iron
Serve with brown rice.

· prune mousse ·
serves 4

School dinners did all they could to dampen the reputation of
prunes – quite unfairly! This sugar-free mousse is very simple
and quick to make. A great favourite with adults and children
alike. Do not waste time stoning prunes – you can buy pitted
prunes in health shops.

---

8 oz (225 g) pitted prunes
2 free-range eggs, separated
5 oz (140 g) natural low-fat yoghurt
1 tablespoon freshly squeezed orange juice
whole walnuts to decorate

Just cover the prunes with water, cover and cook for 10–15
minutes until soft. Keep an eye on the liquid, to make sure
they do not burn.

Drain. Retain the liquid to drink. Put the prunes in a
blender and purée until smooth. Separate the eggs and beat
in the egg yolks and yoghurt, then mix in the orange juice.

Whisk the egg whites until stiff and fold into the mixture.

65

Spoon into individual bowls, smooth the surface, cover and chill. Decorate with walnuts to serve.

To help iron absorption
Serve the mousse with slices of fresh orange.

· *fig and orange slices* ·
makes about 16

These filling slices are lovely and moist.

---

12 oz (336 g) dried figs
10 fl oz (300 ml) unsweetened orange juice
grated rind of two oranges
8 oz (225 g) plain wholemeal flour
4 oz (112 g) rolled oats
5 oz (140 g) unsalted butter or polyunsaturated
  margarine
2 tablespoons clear honey

Preheat the oven to 200°C (400°F, Mark 6) and lightly grease a 11 × 7 in (28 × 18 cm) shallow cake tin.

Put the figs in a medium saucepan, with the orange juice and orange rind. Cover and heat very gently for about 20 minutes until the figs are soft. Stir occasionally and watch carefully because the natural sugar in the figs makes them likely to burn. Cool slightly, then put in a liquidizer with any juice remaining and blend until smooth.

In another pan, melt the butter or margarine and honey over a gentle heat. Remove from the heat then stir in the flour and oats, mixing well. Spread half this mixture evenly over the cake tin. Press well in. Cover with the figs, then sprinkle the remaining oat mixture over the top. Press down firmly.

Bake for 20–25 minutes until golden brown. Allow to cool in the tin before cutting into slices. Store in an airtight container or freeze.

· *fruit sweets* ·

makes about 40

Despite their slightly unusual appearance, these sugar-free sweets are very popular with children. Use any fruit juice concentrate from a health shop.

---

3 oz (84 g) pumpkin seeds
3 oz (84 g) sunflower seeds
2 oz (56 g) unsulphured dried peaches
2 oz (56 g) unsulphured dried apricots
2 oz (56 g) dried figs
2 oz (56 g) pitted prunes
5 fl oz (150 ml) unsweetened orange juice
$\frac{1}{4}$ teaspoon mixed spice
2 tablespoons fruit juice concentrate

Finely grind the seeds in a food processor or grinder. (Put these aside.)

Add the fruit to the processor, making sure each individual fruit is separated, otherwise they tend to stick together. Add the orange juice and mixed spice. Finely chop the fruit until you have a soft, sticky mixture, but do not let it go runny. Add the concentrated fruit juice and process for a further minute, then pour in the ground seeds and mix in well. Remove from the processor and with your hands work the mixture into small balls, about $\frac{1}{2}$ in (1.3 cm) in diameter. Arrange on a large flat plate or glass baking sheet and chill for at least an hour. Serve immediately or transfer to an airtight container.

· *peach and walnut tart* ·

serves 4–6

The unusual combination of peach and walnut makes this tart rather special. You can buy unsulphured dried peaches in health shops. They normally need soaking, otherwise they are quite dry and tough.

6 oz (168 g) unsulphured dried peaches
3 oz (84 g) shelled walnuts
7 oz (196 g) natural low-fat yoghurt
2 free-range eggs
3 tablespoons clear honey
$\frac{1}{4}$ teaspoon ground cinnamon
$\frac{1}{4}$ teaspoon ground nutmeg
2 tablespoons freshly squeezed lemon juice

For the crust
wholemeal shortcrust pastry, made with 7 oz (196 g) flour
(see p. 253)

Soak the peaches for about an hour to soften. Drain and retain the liquid for use elsewhere. Chop into $\frac{3}{4}$ in (2 cm) pieces.

Preheat the oven to 200°C (400°F, Mark 6). Roll the pastry out thinly and use to line a lightly greased 8 in (20 cm) flan tin. Flute the edges with a fork. Chop the walnuts and spread evenly, with the peaches, over the base of the pastry case.

Beat together the yoghurt, eggs, honey and spices in a small bowl, then mix in the lemon juice. Pour the mixture evenly over the walnuts and peaches. Bake for 15 minutes. Reduce the heat to 180°C (350°F, Mark 4) and cook for a further 25–30 minutes until the pastry is crisp and the filling is set or golden brown. Serve hot or cold.

8

•

ZINC

•

Zinc plays an important part in practically every aspect of physical, mental and sexual development. Required in large amounts because it cannot be stored to any great extent in the body, it is essential for many metabolic processes: the utilization of carbohydrates, fats and certain vitamins; the formation of blood, various enzymes and hormones; the correct functioning of respiratory processes.

Zinc is required for the expression of genetic potential, as it has a vital role in the formation of RNA and DNA, and is essential for the proper development of the foetus – in particular, its immune system and the development of its brain.

It is used in wound healing and greatly affects the efficiency of the immune system and the senses of taste, smell and vision. It is also necessary for the development of sexual characteristics, the production of sperm and many other male and female reproductive processes.

How zinc relates to other substances

Zinc is essential for the metabolism of vitamin A. Its absorption is promoted by vitamin D and helped by the citrates contained in some citrus fruits, such as oranges.

Other minerals, such as calcium, copper and phosphorus, tend to oppose the action of zinc. Iron supplements given to pregnant women can interfere with zinc absorption.

Some toxic metals, such as cadmium and lead, inhibit the absorption of zinc by attaching themselves to zinc-dependent enzymes. This prevents them from doing their job of breaking down and metabolizing foodstuffs, repairing tissues and utilizing energy.

Many high-fibre foods, such as soya proteins and breakfast cereals with a high bran content, contain *phytates*, which tend to inhibit the absorption of zinc from the intestine, especially if they are eaten with calcium-rich foods such as cow's milk and cheese. Most experts advise not to eat more than 2 heaped tablespoons of raw bran per day.

Refined and processed foods, like hamburgers, which are high in *phosphates*, also inhibit zinc absorption. Tea and coffee can affect absorption of zinc, especially if they are drunk with a meal.

Signs of deficiency

There are many different symptoms of zinc deficiency including: white spots on the finger nails, slow growth, hair loss, diarrhoea, skin conditions, reduced resistance to infection, immune deficiencies, impaired wound healing, impaired sense of taste and smell, low sperm count, male infertility, sensitivity to light, night blindness, inability to concentrate, and sleep and behavioural disturbances. A rare condition, known as *acrodermatitis enteropathica*, mainly suffered by very young babies when they are weaned, is also caused by zinc deficiency.

THOSE MOST AT RISK OF DEFICIENCY

Many people are at risk of zinc deficiency either because their dietary intake is insufficient or because, although they eat enough zinc, they do not absorb it properly. Others lose zinc or have increased needs because of their particular condition. Some of those most likely to need more are:

- Vegetarians. Because plant foods contain only small quantities of zinc, some vegetarians may not have enough in their diet. However, the citrates in citrus fruits like oranges should help zinc absorption.

- Smokers. Their absorption is likely to be poor, because cigarettes contain large quantities of cadmium which inhibits zinc absorption.

- Alcoholics. Alcohol serves to decrease the absorption of zinc into the intestine and also increases excretion of zinc in the urine.

- Those on certain drugs, including steroids, diuretics, ethanol, anti-convulsant drugs and laxatives.

- Some women on the contraceptive pill.

- Pregnant women, especially in the last few months of pregnancy where zinc is required for the proper development of the (foetal) immune system. Pregnant women also need extra zinc if they are taking iron supplements.

- Breast-feeding women, because the baby rapidly uses up the mother's supply of zinc.

- Those on exclusion diets for food allergies.

- Those on extreme slimming diets.

- Those on high-fibre diets.

- The elderly.

- Those living in areas of high lead pollution, for example, on a busy road.

- Hyperactive children. It is possible that because of a zinc deficiency, these children absorb too much lead, which leads to behavioural problems.

A zinc deficiency may also arise due to excessive sweating, prolonged exercise, hormonal changes and stress. It can also result in a loss of the sense of smell.

Therapeutic uses

Extra zinc has been used successfully to treat many conditions associated with zinc deficiency. These conditions include:

- Hair loss. Extra zinc has helped to reverse hair loss in those suffering from alopecia.

- Wound healing. Zinc ointment has been used for years to help heal wounds, and extra zinc has been found to speed up the healing process of surgical wounds.

- Rheumatoid arthritis and other inflammatory conditions. Some patients given extra zinc experimentally showed a marked improvement in joint swelling and tenderness, morning stiffness and other symptoms.

- Anorexia nervosa. Many sufferers given zinc supplements have made a complete recovery.

- Low immune response. Zinc has been shown to be of benefit to people with a reduced resistance to infection, for example, those suffering from bereavement or the after-effects of a viral infection such as glandular fever. Because zinc deficiency has been observed in people suffering from a wide variety of conditions, including TB, kidney disease and cancer, it is possible that zinc supplementation could be of use in these conditions.

- The common cold. Some people find that sucking zinc gluconate lozenges helps to reduce the duration of the common cold.

- Impaired senses of vision and taste. Those suffering from night blindness due to zinc deficiency and those with an impaired or disordered sense of taste have been helped by extra zinc.

Sources of zinc

Food	Mg per 100 g	Food	Mg per 100 g
Oysters	45.0 a	Egg yolk	3.6
Wheatgerm	17.0	Dried peas	3.5
Wheat bran	16.2	Chicken liver	3.4
Sesame seeds	10.3 b	Oatmeal	3.3
Dried yeast	8.0	Pot barley	3.3
Calf's liver	7.8	Anchovies, canned in oil, fish only	3.2
Whelks, boiled	7.2	Dried rosemary	3.2
Alfalfa	6.9 **	Almonds	3.1
Cocoa powder	6.9	Lentils	3.1
Pig's liver	6.9	Camembert cheese	3.0
Ground ginger	6.8	Walnuts	3.0
Winkles, boiled	5.7	Indian tea	3.0
Crab, boiled	5.5	Peanut butter	3.0
Anise seeds	5.3	Peanuts	3.0
Shrimps, boiled	5.3	Rye flour	3.0
Dill seeds	5.2	Sardines, canned in oil, fish only	3.0
Sunflower seeds	5.2 **	Wholemeal flour	2.9
Coriander seeds	4.7	Butter beans	2.8
Oats	4.5 **	Haricot beans	2.8
Beef	4.3	Red kidney beans	2.8
Brazil nuts	4.2	Buckwheat	2.6
Curry powder	4.1	Pig's kidney	2.6
Dried skimmed milk	4.1	Bacon	2.5
Wheat	4.1 **	Hazelnuts	2.4
Cheddar cheese	4.0	Lamb's kidney	2.4
Edam cheese	4.0	Pork	2.4
Lamb	4.0	Lamb's heart	2.0
Ox liver	4.0	Brown rice	1.8
Parmesan cheese	4.0	Lobster, boiled	1.8
Split peas	4.0	Wholemeal bread	1.8
Lamb's liver	3.9	Tomato paste	1.7
Aduki beans	3.8 **		

Sources of zinc

Food	Mg per 100 g	Food	Mg per 100 g
Mussels	1.6	Spaghetti	1.5
Pilchards in tomato sauce	1.6	Rye	1.3**
Prawns, boiled	1.6	Cockles, boiled	1.2
Eggs	1.5	Squid, frozen	1.2
Macaroni	1.5	Sweetcorn on the cob	1.2
Noodles	1.5		

Notes:

a Oysters are likely to be polluted with cadmium and lead, which means that the value of their zinc content is likely to be cancelled out. Canned fish such as anchovies and cod roes may also contain lead from the solder used to seal the tips.

b Pumpkin seeds also contain zinc but information on the exact content is not available.

· *crab salad* ·

serves 4

A quick, nutritious salad to make when fresh crab is out of season. Frozen white and brown crab meat from a fishmonger is usually free from preservatives and colouring. Tinned crab meat usually contains sugar, salt, colouring and preservatives so it requires a good rinse before use.

---

8 oz (225 g) white crab meat, defrosted if frozen, **or**
2 6 oz (168 g) tins white crab meat, drained and rinsed
3 tablespoons mayonnaise (see p. 247)
2 small green chillies
2 tablespoons freshly chopped chives
2 tablespoons freshly squeezed lime juice
pinch ginger
dash hot chilli sauce
freshly ground black pepper
crisp lettuce leaves
pinch paprika
3 free-range eggs, hard-boiled

Garnish
lime or lemon wedges
sprigs of fresh dill weed or parsley

Flake the crab meat into a medium-sized bowl. Mix in the mayonnaise.

Top and tail the chillies, slit the sides and remove the seeds. Finely chop the chillies and chives. Add to the crab with the lime juice, ginger and chilli sauce, season with pepper, and mix in well.

Wash the lettuce leaves and dry in a salad-spinner or pat dry with kitchen paper. Place them on a medium-sized, flat serving plate. Arrange the crab in the middle of the lettuce leaves. Sprinkle with paprika.

Shell and thinly slice the eggs. Arrange the egg slices and lemon or lime wedges on the lettuce leaves, around the crab. Place several sprigs of dill or parsley on top of the crab and serve immediately.

For extra zinc
Serve with pieces of hot wholemeal pitta bread or with brown rice.

· *barley salad* ·
serves 4

Barley is a good grain for a salad, because it is chewy. Buy the whole grain, that is, pot barley, from a health shop. I like this salad warm, with the cheese freshly melted.

---

6 oz (168 g) pot (wholegrain) barley
3 oz (84 g) Cheddar cheese, grated
3 oz (84 g) sunflower seeds
3 medium tomatoes
2 sticks celery
1 clove garlic
sea salt
freshly ground black pepper

Rinse the barley under cold running water, then put it in a large saucepan, cover with plenty of boiling water, return to the boil, cover and simmer for 40–50 minutes until soft. The barley will expand a great deal and will absorb a lot of water, so keep an eye on the water level and add more to prevent sticking, if necessary. (If using a pressure cooker, cover with plenty of water, bring to the boil and simmer for 20 minutes.) Drain. While the barley is still warm, mix in the cheese and the sunflower seeds.

Thinly slice the tomatoes and celery, crush the garlic and mix in well. Season with salt and pepper and serve immediately.

· spicy peanut spread with alfalfa ·
enough for 4–6 sandwiches

A popular spread for lunch-box sandwiches. I often pack this into halves of wholemeal pitta bread, with tomatoes, extra green pepper and other salad vegetables. It serves well as a party dip too. You can buy alfalfa sprouts in supermarkets. Better still, sprout your own.

---

5 oz (140 g) natural low-fat yoghurt
2 tablespoons smooth peanut butter, sugar-free
1 teaspoon curry powder
pinch chilli powder
2 oz (56 g) Cheddar cheese, grated
1 clove garlic
1 small green pepper
2 oz (56 g) alfalfa sprouts
3 oz (84 g) sunflower seeds

Mix together the yoghurt, peanut butter, curry and chilli powders and cheese in a medium bowl.

Crush the garlic. Remove the top from the pepper, take out the core and seeds but not the pith, and chop very finely. Separate the alfalfa sprouts. Add the garlic, pepper, alfalfa and sunflower seeds and mix in well.

For extra zinc
Cut 2 slices of wholemeal pitta bread in half. Gently open each half and divide the spread evenly between them. Add tomatoes and green peppers to make a filling sandwich.

· meat balls in tomato sauce ·
makes about 24

This tasty Italian dish makes an ideal main course for a family, or to serve to friends.

---

2 oz (56 g) wholemeal bread
4 fl oz (120 ml) skimmed milk
1 lb (450 g) lean minced beef
1 small onion
2 tablespoons fresh parsley
2 cloves garlic
2 oz (56 g) grated Parmesan
$\frac{1}{4}$ teaspoon ground nutmeg
$\frac{1}{2}$ teaspoon dried oregano
grated rind of half a lemon
2 free-range eggs, beaten
sea salt
freshly ground black pepper
$1\frac{1}{2}$–2 pts (900–1,200 ml) tomato sauce (see p. 249)
2 bay leaves
bouquet garni

For coating
wholemeal flour

For shallow-frying
unrefined, cold-pressed sunflower oil

Cut the crusts off the bread and soak it in the milk in a large mixing bowl for 5 minutes. Squeeze the bread dry, discard the remaining milk and return the bread to the bowl. Add the meat and mix in well.

Finely chop the onion and the parsley and crush the garlic. Add the onion, parsley, garlic, cheese, nutmeg, oregano, lemon rind and beaten eggs, season with salt and pepper and mix in well. Shape the mixture into balls, about 1 in (2.5 cm) in diameter. Spread out the flour on a clean surface and coat each meat ball thoroughly on all sides. Cover and refrigerate while you make the tomato sauce.

Put the oil in a heavy-based pan, to a depth of about $\frac{1}{4}$ in (6 mm) and heat it. Gently fry the meatballs in batches for 3–4 minutes, turning regularly, until lightly browned on all sides. Remove with a slotted spoon. Drain on kitchen paper.

Heat the tomato sauce in a large pan, adding the bay leaves and the bouquet garni. Add more oregano and basil if desired. Place the meat balls in the sauce, bring to the boil, cover and simmer gently for 15–20 minutes. (If the sauce seems to be sticking, add more water.) Serve immediately.

For extra zinc
Serve with hot wholemeal spaghetti or tagliatelle, and sprinkle with Parmesan cheese.

· *lentil and hazelnut rissoles* ·
makes 14–18

Lentils and nuts together provide a complete source of protein. Serve with tomato or yoghurt sauces (see pp. 249, 250) or onion gravy (see p. 252).

---

8 oz (225 g) whole brown lentils
6 oz (168 g) shelled hazelnuts
2 oz (56 g) wheatgerm
1 medium onion
2 cloves garlic
1 medium red pepper
1 oz (28 g) unsalted butter or polyunsaturated sunflower
   margarine
3 tablespoons fresh parsley
2 tablespoons tomato purée
$\frac{1}{2}$ teaspoon paprika
$\frac{1}{4}$ teaspoon cayenne pepper
$\frac{1}{4}$ teaspoon chilli powder

freshly squeezed juice of half a lemon
sea salt
freshly ground black pepper
2 free-range eggs, beaten

For coating
2 oz (56 g) fine oatmeal

For shallow-frying
unrefined, cold-pressed sunflower oil

Wash and pick over the lentils and remove any grit. Put them in a pan, cover with boiling water, return to the boil and simmer for 25–40 minutes until just tender. (If using a pressure cooker, cover with fresh water, bring to the boil and simmer for 10–15 minutes.) Drain. Put in a food processor and grind coarsely. Alternatively, mash with a fork. Finely grind the hazelnuts in a food processor or grinder and mix with the lentils and the wheatgerm. If you are using the oven to cook the rissoles, pre-heat to 180°C (350°F, Mark 4).

Chop the onion finely and crush the garlic. Remove the top from the red pepper, taking out the seeds but not the core or pith, and finely chop. Melt the butter or margarine in a frying pan, put in the onion, garlic and red pepper, cover and cook until soft. Chop the parsley. Add the parsley, tomato purée, paprika, cayenne pepper, chilli powder and lemon juice and mix in well. Season with salt and pepper.

Remove from the heat and combine with the lentil mixture. Mix in well, shape into flat rissoles and dip each one into the beaten egg. Spread the oatmeal out on to a clean surface and coat each rissole on both sides. Put the oil in a heavy-based pan to a depth of ¼ in (6 mm) and gently fry for 5–7 minutes until golden brown on both sides. Remove with a slotted spoon and drain on kitchen paper. Alternatively, bake in the middle of the oven on a lightly greased baking sheet, covered with foil, for 20 minutes, turning once. Serve immediately.

For extra zinc
Serve with pot barley or brown rice.

· *beef lasagne* ·
serves 4–6

Lasagne is a simple, popular dish that only needs a light salad to accompany it. Use no-pre-cook lasagne for speed. You need a large ovenproof dish that is at least 2 in (5 cm) deep for this lasagne. Serve with a green salad or steamed vegetables.

---

1 large onion
2 cloves garlic
1 oz (28 g) unsalted butter or polyunsaturated margarine
1¼ lb (562 g) finely ground minced beef
1 14 oz (392 g) tin tomatoes
2 tablespoons tomato purée
5 fl oz (150 ml) water
freshly ground black pepper
1 pt (600 ml) cheese sauce (see p. 251)
12 sheets no-pre-cook wholewheat lasagne
1½ oz (42 g) grated Parmesan

Finely chop the onion and crush the garlic. Melt the butter or margarine in a heavy-based pan on a gentle heat, put in the onion and garlic, cover and cook for 5 minutes. Add the meat and cook, stirring occasionally, until brown. Add the tinned tomatoes, tomato purée and water, cover, bring to the boil and simmer gently for 20 minutes. Season with pepper. (There should be enough salt with the tinned tomatoes and the purée.) Preheat the oven to 200°C (400°F, Mark 6). Five minutes before the meat is done, make the cheese sauce.

Spread one layer of meat over the base of the ovenproof dish then one layer of lasagne on top of the meat, breaking it if necessary to fit your dish. Now add one layer of cheese sauce. Repeat this twice, finishing with a layer of cheese sauce. Sprinkle the grated Parmesan over the top. Cook in the oven for 20–25 minutes until bubbling, and the top is golden brown. Serve immediately.

· *aduki bean slices* ·

serves 4–6

Aduki beans have a nutty sort of flavour that goes really well with most other foods. Here, with brown rice, they make a complete form of protein. These slices are ideal for picnics served with lots of green salad, or hot with vegetables.

---

4 oz (100 g) aduki beans

8 oz (225 g) short-grain brown rice

1 small onion

2 tablespoons freshly chopped parsley

2 large carrots

1 tablespoon unrefined, cold-pressed olive oil

1 tablespoon freshly chopped rosemary or 2 tablespoons dried rosemary

2 tablespoons tamari (soy sauce)

4 oz (112 g) Cheddar cheese, grated

2 free-range eggs, beaten

Soak the beans overnight. Drain. Put in a pan, cover with boiling water (about double their volume), return to the boil, cover and fast-boil for 10 minutes. Reduce the heat and simmer gently for a further 25 minutes or until soft. (If using a pressure cooker, bring to the boil and simmer for 15 minutes.) Drain.

At the same time, wash the rice, put in a pan, cover with boiling water, return to the boil, cover and simmer for 15 minutes until soft but crunchy. Drain and rinse. Preheat the oven to 190°C (375°F, Mark 5) and lightly grease a 7 × 9 in (18 × 23 cm) baking tin.

When the beans are nearly done, finely chop the onion and parsley, and grate the carrots. Put the olive oil in a large frying pan, add the onion, cover and cook gently until soft. Add the drained beans and rice and heat through. Add the parsley, rosemary and carrots, mix in well and heat through again. Mix in the tamari, then the grated cheese, allowing it to melt.

Remove from the heat and add the beaten eggs. Mix all the ingredients in well. Transfer the mixture to the baking tin, spread evenly and press well in. Bake for 30 minutes until firm. Leave to cool in the tin, then cut into 8 slices. Serve hot or cold.

· sesame and oat squares ·

makes about 9

These squares are a real winner with children and adults alike. They are ideal for children's parties or for afternoon tea. They are simple and quick to make. Jumbo oats are available from a health shop. If you cannot find them, use rolled oats.

---

2 oz (56 g) sesame seeds

3 oz (84 g) jumbo oats

1 oz (28 g) wheatgerm

2 oz (56 g) raisins

2 fl oz (60 ml) unrefined, cold-pressed sunflower oil

2 tablespoons clear honey

1 free-range egg, beaten

Preheat the oven to 180°C (350°F, Mark 4). Lightly grease an 8 in (20 cm) square shallow cake tin.

Mix together the sesame seeds, oats, wheatgerm and raisins in a bowl. Add the oil, honey and beaten egg. Mix thoroughly. Transfer the mixture to the cake tin, spread evenly and press well in.

Bake in the middle of the oven for 30–35 minutes until golden brown.

Allow to cool for a few minutes then cut into squares, but cool completely before removing from the tin. Store in an airtight container or freeze.

· fig and banana purée with pumpkin seeds ·

serves 4

There is no sugar in this dessert, but it is very filling. Most supermarkets sell natural fromage frais and you will find pumpkin seeds in a health shop.

---

5 oz (140 g) dried figs
2 large bananas
freshly squeezed juice of half a lemon
4 oz (112 g) low-fat natural fromage frais (fromage blanc)
1 oz (28 g) pumpkin seeds

Just cover the figs with water, cover, bring to the boil and simmer gently for 20 minutes or until soft. Check the water level regularly and add more if necessary to prevent sticking. Drain, retaining the water to use elsewhere.

Put the figs into a liquidizer and blend to a smooth purée. Mash the bananas with a fork, add the lemon juice and mix in well with the figs. Spoon into small individual glass bowls, cover and chill.

Just before serving, spoon a large blob of fromage frais on top of each portion. Sprinkle with pumpkin seeds and serve immediately.

· sunflower carob biscuits ·

makes about 20

These light biscuits are popular with children. They expand considerably in cooking so do not be tempted to put them too close.

---

4 oz (112 g) unsalted butter or polyunsaturated margarine
2 oz (56 g) raw light muscovado sugar
1 free-range egg, beaten
4 oz (112 g) wholemeal self-raising flour
2 teaspoons carob powder

83

1–2 teaspoons skimmed milk
3 oz (84 g) sunflower seeds

Preheat the oven to 180°C (350°F, Mark 4). Lightly grease two baking sheets.

Cream together the butter or margarine and the sugar until light and fluffy. Add the egg and beat in thoroughly, until you have a creamy consistency. Gradually mix in the flour and the carob powder, and add a little milk, if necessary, to make the mixture soft and creamy, then mix in the sunflower seeds.

Work into balls, about 1 in (2.5 cm) in diameter. Place on the baking sheets, with plenty of room in between to expand, and press flat with a palette knife. Bake in the middle of the oven for 10–15 minutes until golden brown.

Leave to cool slightly, then carefully transfer to a wire rack and leave for approximately 5 minutes. Store in an airtight container.

9

·

POTASSIUM

·

Potassium is present in every cell of the body and is important for a wide range of bodily functions. It is essential for the correct working of the heart, the muscles and the nervous system and for the maintenance of normal blood glucose levels.

Potassium works with sodium to control body water and the balance of the two minerals is regulated by the kidneys through excretion in the urine. About 90 per cent of potassium is absorbed from the diet and most of it stays inside the body cells.

Signs of deficiency

These include muscle fatigue, loss of appetite, irritability, swelling of the feet and ankles, bone and joint pains, headaches, muscle cramps, apathy and irregular heartbeat. In severe cases, heart failure may result. Low potassium intake can also predispose you to high blood pressure.

THOSE MOST AT RISK OF DEFICIENCY

- Anyone with an excessive intake of salt.
- Anyone with chronic diarrhoea.
- Anyone taking diuretics which can cause potassium loss.
- Regular users of laxatives.

- Those with certain gastro-intestinal disorders.
- Those on certain drugs including steroids and aspirin.

Therapeutic uses

Those with high blood pressure often have a high sodium: potassium ratio in their bodies. Eating potassium-rich foods, with little or no salt, normally helps to restore the balance. Potassium depletion can also be helped by taking fruit juices or home-made vegetable soup several times a day.

LOSSES FROM FOOD

Modern methods of food processing such as canning and freezing cause serious losses of potassium. Loss is also increased by using large quantities of water and salt in cooking. It is therefore advisable to steam vegetables or use a minimal amount of water, and to avoid using salt, especially if you have high blood pressure.

Sources of potassium

Food	Mg per 100 g	Food	Mg per 100 g
Dulse	8,060 a	Kidney beans	1,160
Wakame	6,800 b	Broad beans	1,123
Arame	3,860 c	Dried peaches	1,100
Blackstrap molasses	2,927*	Parsley	1,080
Carragheen	2,844 d	Dried figs	1,010
Dried apricots	1,880	Almonds	860
Butter beans	1,700	Dried prunes	860
Soya beans	1,677	Raisins	860
Soya flour	1,660	Sultanas	860
Tomato purée	1,540	Mung beans	850
Chinese mushrooms, dried	1,482	Chickpeas	800
Red chillies	1,286	Brazil nuts	760
Haricot beans	1,160	Desiccated coconut	750

Food	Mg per 100 g	Food	Mg per 100 g
Dried dates	750	Mackerel	360
Currants	710	Bananas	350
Peanut Butter	700	Beef	350
Walnuts	690	Cauliflower	350
Blackeye beans	688	Hazelnuts	350
Peanuts	680	Lamb	350
Globe artichoke	673	Passion fruit	350
Lentils	670	Broccoli tops	340
Potatoes, old	570	Herring	340
Pot barley	560	Parsnips	340
No-pre-cook lasagne verdi	540e	Peas	340
Kipper, baked	520	Wholemeal flour	340
Sprats	512	Prawns	333
Chestnuts	500	Calf's liver	330
Mushrooms	470	Apricots	320
Spinach	470	Cantaloupe melon	320
Cashew nuts	464	Chicken	320
Bloater, grilled	450	Cod	320
Coconut	440	Grapes, black	320
Rhubarb	430	Whelks, boiled	320
Sardines, canned in oil, fish only	430	Greengages	310
Pilchards, canned in tomato sauce	420	Leeks	310
Stoneground wholewheat pasta	420f	Pumpkin	310
Rye flour	410	Salmon	310
Sesame seeds	407	Watercress	310
Avocados	400	Chicken liver	300
Celeriac, boiled	400	Haddock	300
Plantain	400	Sweetcorn on the cob	300
Garlic	373	Duck	290
Blackcurrants	370	Tomatoes	290
Pork	370	Cabbage, white	280
Sweet potato	370	Celery	280
Trout, steamed	370	Cherries	280

Food	Mg per 100 g	Food	Mg per 100 g
Plaice	280	Tuna, canned in oil	280
Redcurrants	280	Crab, boiled	270
Runner beans	280	Lamb's kidney	270

Notes:

a,b,c and **d** Information taken from *Vegetables from the Sea* by Teruko and Seibin Arasaki.

e and **f** Information supplied by Record Pasta Ltd.

I have not included recipes for potassium.

10

•

INTRODUCTION TO
VITAMINS

•

Vitamins are organic substances that are required in small amounts for the normal biochemical functioning of our bodies. They are absolutely essential for life.

Vitamins are usually defined according to three criteria:

1   They cannot be made by body tissue and must be obtained from the diet.

2   Deficiency of a vitamin in the body leads to certain clinical and biochemical symptoms, some general and some specific.

3   These symptoms and signs of deficiency are reversed by treatment only with the appropriate vitamin.

Inevitably, there are exceptions. For example, vitamin D can be synthesized in the skin and nicotinic acid (B_3) can be made in the liver. Many vitamins are also produced by intestinal bacteria.

Many vitamins are present in enzymes, the natural catalysts on which all life's processes depend. These processes include: the digestion of food and converting this food into energy; maintenance and repair of body tissues; functioning of all vital organs; maintaining healthy blood; skeletal, muscle and nerve functions; protecting the body against toxins and other damaging influences such as pollution, and protection against infections, viruses and major diseases like cancer, heart disease and arthritis.

There are two major groups of vitamins: the water-soluble ones – the B vitamins and vitamin C – that are required on a daily basis, and the fat-soluble ones – A, D, E and K – that can be stored more readily in the body.

The vitamin B complex has eight main constituents: thiamine (B_1), riboflavin (B_2), nicotinic acid (B_3), pantothenic acid (B_5), pyridoxine (B_6), cyanocobalamin (B_{12}), folic acid and biotin. It also includes: choline, inositol, para-aminobenzoic acid and orotic acid (B_{13}). These are essential nutrients, vital for health, but they are not generally regarded as vitamins mainly because the body can make them. Two other nutrients, pangamic acid and laetrile, complete the B complex list.

The vitamin C complex also includes bioflavanoids – rutin, hesperidin and citrus bioflavanoids – which used to be called vitamin P. These are important nutrients that accompany vitamin C in food and work with it to maintain our health and vitality.

LOSSES FROM FOOD
Most vitamins are extremely sensitive and are easily lost through processing, preparing and cooking food. (See individual chapters for details.)

DAILY NEEDS
Everybody's vitamin requirements are different. They are dependent on all sorts of factors and may change. This makes it very difficult to tell how much a given person needs at any one time. (See individual chapters for more information.)

TOXIC DOSAGES
Excessive intakes of most water-soluble vitamins are generally excreted in the urine. However, adverse side-effects have been reported for vitamin B_3 and many women taking high dosages of vitamin B_6 for premenstrual syndrome have reported a variety of adverse side-effects. Vitamin C in excessive dosages can also be dangerous.

Excessive intakes of fat-soluble vitamins accumulate in the body and can be dangerous. *Always consult your doctor before taking high-dosage vitamin supplements.*

11

·

VITAMIN A

·

Vitamin A is a fat-soluble compound, commonly known as retinol. This is found only in foods of animal origin, but other vitamin A-type compounds – the most important of which is beta-carotene – are found in vegetables and fruit, especially those that are orange or yellow in colour. The richer or darker the colour, the greater the beta-carotene content; the outer leaves of vegetables usually contain the most.

Vitamin A is essential for the normal functioning of the eye, especially the light-sensitive areas that help the eyes adjust in dim light or darkness. It is necessary to prevent corneal changes and xerophthalmia, a disease that causes drying of the eye.

It is required for the synthesis of proteins involved in the building and repairing of body cells, tissues and organs. It is especially important for the maintenance of tissues lining the mouth, and the respiratory and urinary tracts. Vitamin A is essential for normal reproductive functions, growth and bone maintenance and it is also involved in regulating the balance of bodily fluids.

It has a key role in boosting the body's natural ability to resist infection. Vitamin A and, in particular, beta-carotene act as anti-oxidants to protect the body cells against the destructive action of free radicals. These are toxic by-products of oxygen that are produced during normal metabolic processes. They also result directly or indirectly from radiation, atmospheric pollutants, such as car fumes and tobacco smoke, and from some constituents in the diet. They float around the body, looking for something to attach themselves to. They begin to destroy tissues and this destruction starts off the degenerative process that is the basis of many diseases.

Signs of deficiency

Vitamin A deficiency is one of the most common and serious worldwide deficiencies. The earliest signs are night blindness or inability to see in dim light, and dryness of the eyes. Sometimes skin blemishes of various kinds such as dry, scaly skin appear, but these may be due to malabsorption of other nutrients. An extreme form of vitamin A deficiency is xerophthalmia, a degenerative condition characterized by ulceration of the eyes and eventual blindness.

In developing countries, vitamin A deficiency is reflected in poor growth and decreased resistance to infection.

THOSE MOST AT RISK OF DEFICIENCY

Severe vitamin A deficiency is extremely rare in developed countries. However, diabetics may be at risk, possibly because they are unable to convert beta-carotene to vitamin A efficiently. Cancer patients have also been found to be low in vitamin A.

TOXIC DOSAGES

Fat-soluble vitamins like vitamin A have the potential to be toxic because they are stored in the body and not excreted in the urine. It is particularly important to observe dosage instructions, especially when giving drops to a baby or taking supplements during pregnancy, since overdoses may cause damage to the foetus. *Always consult your doctor before taking supplements.*

Therapeutic uses

Vitamin A has sometimes been used successfully to treat skin conditions, but because the high doses involved have potential side-effects, it is not an established form of treatment. However, retinoic acid, a derivative of retinol, which does not carry the same potential risks, has been used to treat skin conditions such as eczema, acne and psoriasis.

It has been found to be of some benefit in the prevention and treatment of stress-induced gastric ulcers. Studies have suggested that low intake of vitamin A or beta-carotene may increase susceptibility to certain kinds of cancer, especially lung cancer and those of the respiratory tract. Research into the role of vitamin A and its derivatives in the treatment of cancer is currently underway.

LOSSES FROM FOOD

Retinol and carotenes are sensitive to heat, light and oxygen and their destruction is accelerated by minerals such as copper. However, because they dissolve in fats in food, they are protected, to some extent, by natural anti-oxidants like vitamin E.

Most cooking methods destroy vitamin A. For example, frying destroys 40 per cent of the vitamin in margarine in 5 minutes, 60 per cent in 10 minutes and 70 per cent in 15 minutes. Vitamin A is not lost in cooking water, however, because it is not soluble in water.

Freezing and canning of green vegetables containing mainly beta-carotene, and subsequent cooking, causes 15–20 per cent loss of the vitamin A activity.

Air drying of fruit and vegetables causes losses of 10–20 per cent, and drying in the sun causes virtual destruction of vitamin A.

It is important to keep all carotene-rich fruit and vegetables in a cool, dark place, in airtight conditions. Stir-frying is probably the best method of cooking to avoid loss of vitamin A because although the temperatures are high, the cooking time is minimal.

Sources of vitamin A

Food	Microgram per 100 g retinol equivalents	Food	Microgram per 100 g retinol equivalents
Lamb's liver	18,100.00	Tomato purée	476.67
Cod liver oil	18,000.00	Cream cheese	421.67
Ox liver	16,500.00	Broccoli tops	416.67
Calf's liver	14,600.00	Stilton cheese	408.33
Pig's liver	9,200.00	Egg yolk	400.00
Nori	3,840.00 a	Vine leaves	383.33
Liver sausage	2,965.00	Cheddar cheese	363.00
Carrots	2,000.00	Parmesan cheese	357.50
Sorrel	1,290.00 *	Fennel	350.00 *
Eel	1,200.00	Canteloupe	333.33
Parsley	1,166.67	Dried peaches	333.33
Red chillies	1,100.00	Endive	333.33
Chinese leaves	1,090.00	Leeks (leaves)	333.33
Kale, leaves only	1,000.00 *	Danish blue cheese	306.33
Turnip tops, boiled	1,000.00	Feta cheese	270.33
Chicken liver	930.00	Apricots	250.00
Soft margarine	869.00	Pumpkin	250.00
Butter	828.33	Camembert cheese	237.50
Spinach	810.00	Edam cheese	237.50
Polyunsaturated margarine	800.00	Single cream	220.33
Ghee	757.33	Mangoes	200.00 c
Hard margarine	717.00	Dried prunes	166.67
Spring greens, boiled	666.67	Lettuce	166.67 d
Sweet poatoes	666.67 b	Spring onions	148.33
Dried apricots	600.00	Eggs	140.00
Watercress	500.00	Sprats, fried	122.00
Double cream	496.67		

Notes:

a Information taken from *Vegetables from the Sea* by Teruko and Seibin Arasaki.

b There is considerable variation according to variety: some yellow sweet potatoes contain 2,000 micrograms of vitamin A, but the white variety contains only a trace.

c This is for ripe, orange-coloured flesh. Unripe green mangoes contain about one-tenth this amount.

d This is an average figure. The outer green leaves may contain fifty times as much carotene as the inner white ones.

For the sake of convenience, the total vitamin A activity in foods has been expressed in retinol equivalents. These take into account the beta-carotene content of foods.

1 retinol equivalent = 1 micrograms retinol
                        = 6 micrograms beta-carotene

Vitamin A activity is also expressed in international units (iu).

1 retinol equivalent = 3.33 iu vitamin A activity from retinol
                        = 10 iu vitamin A activity from beta-carotene

· *carrot and apricot soup* ·

serves 6

This attractive orange-coloured soup has an unusual blend of flavours and it is very filling. Try it out on your friends.

---

1 lb (450 g) carrots
1 medium onion
1 oz (28 g) unsalted butter or polyunsaturated
   margarine
8 oz (225 g) unsulphured dried apricots
2 pts (1,200 ml) vegetable stock
freshly ground pepper
sea salt
5 fl oz (150 ml) single cream (optional)

Garnish
3 tablespoons freshly chopped parsley

Scrub the carrots and slice thinly. Finely chop the onion. Melt the butter or margarine in a large saucepan over a gentle heat. Add the carrots and onion. Cover and cook gently for about 5 minutes. Add the apricots and stock. Bring to the boil, cover and simmer for 20 minutes, or until the carrots and apricots are soft. Stir occasionally, and add more water if necessary. Transfer to a blender and purée until smooth. Season with salt and pepper. Transfer to a soup tureen. Cover and chill.

Just before serving, stir in the cream if so desired. Chop the parsley and sprinkle over the soup.

· chinese leaf, watercress and peach salad ·

serves 4

The contrast of colours and texture makes this an attractive salad for summer or winter. Use dried apricots or nectarines (available in health shops) instead of peaches, if you prefer. Fennel makes an interesting alternative to Chinese leaf. You can buy fennel seeds in a health shop or from Asian grocers.

---

6 oz (168 g) unsulphured dried peaches
4 tablespoons sweet and sour dressing (see p. 242)
8 oz (225 g) Chinese leaf
1 bunch of watercress
2 teaspoons whole fennel seeds

Soak the peaches overnight in a covered bowl, in the fridge. Drain and retain the liquid to use elsewhere.

If you forget to soak the peaches, put them in a pan with the lid on, cover with boiling water, return to the boil and simmer gently for 10–15 minutes until softened. Leave in the covered pan for 1 hour to soften further, then drain. Retain the liquid.

Make the dressing now to avoid extra vitamin loss.

Cut the peaches into $\frac{1}{2}$ in (1.3 cm) cubes and put into a large salad bowl. Cut the Chinese leaf into $\frac{1}{4}$ in (6 mm) strips. (It should fall away into shreds.) Rinse the watercress, pat dry with kitchen paper or spin dry in a salad-spinner. Remove any coarse stalks. Add the Chinese leaf, watercress and fennel seeds to the peaches, and toss the salad in the dressing until it is thoroughly coated. Serve immediately.

· cream of watercress soup ·

serves 4

Serve this soup with wholemeal bread or croutons. If you prefer not to use cream, use 15 fl oz (450 ml) milk and 15 fl oz (450 ml) stock instead.

---

2 bunches watercress
1 medium onion
1 large potato
1 oz (28 g) unsalted butter or polyunsaturated
  margarine
10 fl oz (300 ml) skimmed milk
1 pt (600 ml) vegetable stock
sea salt
freshly ground black pepper
5 fl oz (150 ml) single cream

Wash the watercress under cold running water, then dry in a salad-spinner or pat dry with kitchen paper. Break off the rough stalks and chop coarsely. Set the leaves aside, keeping a few for the garnish.

Chop the onion finely. Peel the potatoes, keeping the peelings to use in vegetable stock, and dice into ½ in (1.3 cm) cubes. Heat the butter or margarine in a large saucepan over a gentle heat, add the onion, cover and cook until transparent. Add the potato and watercress stalks, stirring to make sure they are covered in fat, cover and cook for a few more minutes. Stir in the milk and stock, cover and bring to the boil. Simmer gently for 15 minutes or until the potatoes are soft. Mix in the watercress leaves.

Transfer to a blender and purée until smooth. Return to the pan, season with salt and pepper and heat through.

Just before serving, stir in the cream and gently heat through. Check the seasoning. Transfer to a warm soup tureen, garnish with the reserved watercress leaves and serve immediately.

· pumpkin potage ·
serves 6

This is a thick, substantial soup – ideal for long winter evenings round an open fire. Serve with hot garlic bread.

---

2 lb (900 g) pumpkin
6 oz (168 g) potatoes
3 medium carrots
1 large onion
1 oz (28 g) unsalted butter or polyunsaturated
   sunflower margarine
2 pts (1,200 ml) vegetable stock
½ teaspoon paprika
sea salt
freshly ground black pepper
freshly chopped parsley

Peel the pumpkin with a sharp knife and keep the peelings for vegetable stock. Remove the seeds and discard. Cut the pumpkin into large chunks, about 2 in (5 cm) square. Peel the potatoes if necessary and keep the peelings for use in stock. Chop the potatoes and carrots coarsely, and the onion finely.

Melt the butter or margarine in a large saucepan. Put in the onion, cover and cook gently for a couple of minutes. Add the pumpkin, potato and carrot, mix them round to coat with butter, cover and cook gently for 5 minutes. Stir in the stock, bring to the boil, cover and simmer gently for about 20 minutes until the vegetables are just tender. Add more water if necessary to prevent sticking.

Put the vegetables and their liquid in a blender and purée until smooth. Return to the pan and heat through. If the soup is too thick for your taste, add more stock or skimmed milk. Add the paprika and season with salt and pepper. Transfer to a soup tureen. Chop the parsley and sprinkle over the soup. Serve immediately.

· stir-fry liver with orange ·

serves 4

This classic recipe is quick and simple to make, so it is ideal for an evening meal. The secret of cooking liver is to cut it as thinly as possible. Then cook it very quickly for a short time so that it is brown on the outside but pink and tender on the inside. If you overcook it, it becomes tough. Ask your butcher to cut it for you or buy it frozen and cut into thin slivers before it defrosts.

---

1 lb (450 g) lamb's liver

2 tablespoons wholemeal flour

freshly ground black pepper

$\frac{3}{4}$ teaspoon dried sage or 3 teaspoons freshly chopped sage

4 spring onions

1 clove garlic

2 tablespoons freshly chopped parsley

freshly squeezed juice of 1 orange

grated rind of 1 orange

2 oz (56 g) unsalted butter

3 fl oz (90 ml) vegetable stock

5 tablespoons dry sherry

1 teaspoon tamari (soy sauce)

Garnish

additional freshly chopped parsley

Get everything prepared in advance so that you can work quickly to avoid vitamin loss.

Cut the liver into very thin $\frac{1}{4}$ in (6 mm) slices. Spread the flour on a clean surface and season with pepper and sage. Toss the liver in the flour until it is covered all over.

Chop the spring onions finely and crush the garlic. Chop the parsley and prepare the orange. Melt half the butter in a wok or frying pan, get it as hot as you can without burning, and quickly stir-fry the garlic and onions. Remove with a slotted spoon and set aside. Heat the rest of the butter, add the liver and stir-fry for a few minutes until it is crisp and dark on the outside but slightly pink in the middle.

Remove the liver with a slotted spoon and set aside with the onions and garlic. There is no real need to keep them warm because the next stage is very quick and they will be heated again at the last minute.

Add the stock, sherry, tamari, orange juice, orange rind and parsley. Cook on a high heat, stirring constantly until the sauce thickens. Return the liver, onions and garlic to the wok or pan and heat through, stirring all the time. Serve immediately, garnished with freshly-chopped parsley.

For extra vitamin A
Serve with steamed carrots or sweet potatoes or steamed kale, sorrel, spring greens or pumpkin.

· *leek and cheese soufflé* ·
serves 4

Soufflés are very impressive provided you get the timing right, but they sink dramatically after a very short time. Prepare all the ingredients as close to serving as possible and whisk the egg whites at the last minute. Serve with plenty of salad and baked potatoes.

---

2 large leeks
2 tablespoons fresh parsley
1½ oz (42 g) unsalted butter or polyunsaturated margarine
2 oz (56 g) Danish blue cheese, crumbled
freshly ground black pepper
pinch ground nutmeg
1 oz (28 g) plain wholemeal flour
10 fl oz (300 ml) unskimmed milk
3 free-range eggs, separated
2 oz (56 g) Cheddar cheese, grated
pinch Cayenne pepper

Preheat the oven to 190°C (375°F, Mark 5). Lightly grease a 2½ pt (1½ litre) soufflé dish.

Thinly slice the leeks and chop the parsley. Melt half the butter or margarine in a pan, add the leeks, cover and cook until just tender. Mix in the blue cheese until it melts. Remove from the heat and season with pepper and nutmeg.

Heat the rest of the butter in another pan, stir in the flour and cook over a low heat for a few seconds, stirring constantly. Add the milk, and continue to stir until the sauce boils and thickens. Simmer for a couple of minutes. Remove from the heat and beat in the egg yolks, one at a time. Add the leeks, Cheddar cheese, cayenne pepper and parsley. Season with pepper. Mix all the ingredients in well.

Beat the egg whites until stiff. Carefully fold 1 tablespoon of the egg white into the cheese sauce, then gently fold in the remainder. Spoon the mixture into the soufflé dish and bake in the middle of the oven, for about 25 minutes, until risen and golden. The centre should be firm. If it is not, give it another 5 minutes. Serve immediately.

For extra vitamin A
Serve with a green salad; Chinese leaf, watercress and peach or endive salads (see pp. 97, 185) or steamed vegetables such as kale, broccoli or spinach.

· *mango fool* ·
serves 4–6

I only make desserts like this for special occasions, because double cream is very rich in saturated fat and contains lots of calories. You can use yoghurt or low-fat fromage frais to much the same effect if you prefer. Buy ripe mangoes that are soft to the touch when squeezed. Blackcurrants or blackberries are ideal fruits to use as an alternative to mangoes.

---

2 large mangoes
1 tablespoon Cointreau
2 free-range eggs, separated
10 fl oz (300 ml) double cream

Peel the mangoes with a sharp knife over a plate to catch the juice. Cut in half horizontally and scrape the flesh off the stone, directly into your blender, if possible. Mix in the Cointreau and purée until smooth, then beat in the egg yolks.

In a separate large bowl, whisk up the cream until it thickens and gradually fold well into the mangoes. Whisk the egg whites until stiff peaks form, then carefully fold into the mango mixture. Pour into individual glasses or bowls. Cover and chill until required.

· annie's pumpkin pie ·
serves 4–6

This is a perfect dessert for Hallowe'en, when the shops are full to the brim with pumpkins, especially where I live in North London. It is a pity pumpkins are regarded with such contempt in this country, except by keen gardeners. In America they are grown with pride and are displayed in all their glory and variety, at agricultural shows.

---

1 lb (450 g) pumpkin
2 free-range eggs, separated
8 fl oz (240 ml) skimmed milk
$\frac{1}{4}$ teaspoon ground ginger
$\frac{1}{4}$ teaspoon ground nutmeg
$\frac{1}{4}$ teaspoon ground cloves
$1\frac{1}{4}$ teaspoons ground cinnamon
2 oz (56 g) light muscovado sugar
2 oz (56 g) desiccated coconut

For the crust
wholemeal shortcrust pastry made with 7 oz (200 g) flour
    (*see* p. 253)

Preheat the oven to 220°C (425°F, Mark 7).

Roll the pastry out thinly and use to line a 9 in (23 cm) lightly greased flan case. Pinch the edges to decorate. Remove the skin from the pumpkin with a sharp knife and take out the pips. Keep the peelings for use in vegetable stock. Cut into large cubes, about 2 in (5 cm) square. Steam over boiling water, in a covered pan, for about 10 minutes or until just soft. Drain, retaining the liquid for use elsewhere. Mash the pumpkin with a fork, until smooth. Beat together the egg yolks, milk, spices and sugar in a bowl and mix thoroughly with the pumpkin. Whisk the egg whites until stiff peaks form. First fold the whites then the coconut into the mixture and pour into the flan case. Spread evenly. Bake for 10 minutes on 220°C (425°F, Mark 7). Reduce the heat to 190°C (375°F, Mark 5) and bake for a further 20–25 minutes until risen and golden. Serve hot.

For extra vitamin A
Serve with single cream.

12

·

THE
VITAMIN B GROUP:
INTRODUCTION

·

Although the B complex vitamins are chemically distinct from each other, they are interdependent and work together as a group. Essential for the production of energy from food and the metabolism of fats and protein, they are necessary to maintain an efficient digestive system and for the correct functioning of the brain and nervous system.

They contribute to the maintenance of healthy skin, hair, eyes, mouth and liver. Some members of the B complex control the production of haemoglobin, the red pigment in the blood that carries oxygen to the muscles and organs in the body.

Signs of deficiency

It is very unusual to see an isolated deficiency of any *one* of the B vitamins except B_{12}.

The most common general signs of deficiency are: tiredness, irritability, nervous symptoms and mild depression. Skin problems such as psoriasis, eczema and acne may be related to lack of B vitamins, and a poor appetite, insomnia, lethargy, anaemia and constipation can all result from deficiency of the B complex.

It is possible to have a vitamin B deficiency for a long time before any symptoms show. A chronic deficiency may be manifested in mental changes without any physical signs ever appearing.

THOSE MOST AT RISK OF DEFICIENCY

Since the body cannot store the B vitamins, most of us are likely to be short of one or all of them at some time or another. Requirements vary, depending on your level of physical activity, calorie intake, how much alcohol you drink and so on. Needs increase during stress situations, including those produced by infection, and after major surgery.

Some people are particularly susceptible to deficiency:

- Heavy drinkers. Alcohol has an adverse effect on vitamin B metabolism. Because chronic heavy drinkers tend to have a poor diet as well, their vitamin B intake is likely to be low.

- Those who eat a diet high in refined and processed foods.

- Those with a poor diet, for example, the elderly.

- Those on long-term drugs such as anti-convulsants, some antibiotics, etc.

- Women taking the contraceptive pill.

- Anyone with a psychiatric history.

- Pregnant and breast-feeding women.

- Children and adolescents, especially during periods of rapid growth.

- Smokers.

- Those recovering from major surgery.

Therapeutic uses

The vitamin B group control such a wide range of bodily functions that whenever there is a deterioration in health, or mental changes occur, the B vitamins may be beneficial. Because they are so related in function, B vitamins should normally be taken together.

The B complex has been used successfully to treat many conditions including:

- Menstrual problems such as premenstrual tension.

- Behavioural problems in children, such as hyperactivity and schizophrenia.

- Migraines.

- Heart disease. Some people suffering from heart disease have taken the B complex to keep blood cholesterol down to normal levels and to reduce the chances of thrombosis forming.

- Alcoholism. Some alcoholics may benefit from a supplement of the B complex vitamins.

LOSSES FROM FOOD

The main loss of B vitamins occurs through leaching into vegetable cooking water and meat juices, so these should be preserved.

Because thiamine, riboflavin and pantothenic acid are sensitive to alkalis such as baking soda, used as a raising agent in flour, some losses of these vitamins are inevitable in cooking pastry and cakes. Pantothenic acid is also sensitive to acids such as vinegar.

Sulphur dioxide, used as a preservative in dried fruits and foods such as sausages and bacon, causes losses of thiamine.

B vitamins such as pantothenic acid and riboflavin are sensitive to heat, so some losses through cooking are inevitable. Since riboflavin is extremely sensitive to light, every effort should be made to keep food stored in the dark and to cook with the pan lid on.

Thiamine

Sources of thiamine (vitamin B$_1$)

Food	Mg per 100 g	Food	Mg per 100 g
Brewer's yeast	15.60*	Oatmeal	0.50
Sunflower seeds	8.90*	Red pigeon peas	0.50
Millet	3.30*	Wheat flakes	0.50**
Marmite (yeast extract)	3.10	Lamb's kidney	0.49
Wheatgerm	2.01	Lasagne	0.49
Cod's roe	1.50	Bulgur wheat	0.48
Coriander leaves	1.25	Lamb's heart	0.48
Soya beans	1.10	Wholemeal flour	0.47
Alfalfa	1.08*	Broad beans	0.45
Brazil nuts	1.00	Butter beans	0.45
Wholemeal spaghetti	0.99	Cashew nuts	0.45
Peanuts	0.90	Haricot beans	0.45
Pork	0.89	Mung beans	0.45
Wheat bran	0.89	Ox heart	0.45
Soya flour	0.75	Rye	0.43*
Sesame seeds	0.72	Hazelnuts	0.40
Aduki beans	0.70**	Rye flour	0.40
Pistachio nuts	0.70	Chinese mushrooms, dried	0.37
Split peas	0.70	Ox kidney	0.37
Millet flour	0.68	Red chillies	0.37
Bacon	0.65	Chicken liver	0.36
Cumin seeds	0.63	Duck	0.36
Dried peas	0.60	Wholemeal bread	0.34
Rolled oats	0.60*	Peas	0.32
Blackeye beans	0.59	Pig's kidney	0.32
Brown rice	0.59	Pig's liver	0.31
Wheat	0.57*	Pot barley	0.31
Mustard seeds	0.54	Egg yolk	0.30
Red kidney beans	0.54	Plaice	0.30
Chickpeas	0.50	Tomato paste	0.30
Lentils	0.50	Walnuts	0.30

Food	Mg per 100 g	Food	Mg per 100 g
Buckwheat	0.28	Potatoes, old	0.11
Lamb's liver	0.27	Avocados	0.10
Cornmeal	0.26	Broccoli tops	0.10
Noodles	0.26	Brussels sprouts	0.10
Almonds	0.24 a	Cauliflower	0.10
Garlic	0.24	Chicken	0.10
Ox liver	0.23	Crab, boiled	0.10
Calf's liver	0.21	Damsons	0.10
Chestnuts	0.20	Dried prunes	0.10
Couscous	0.20	Leeks	0.10
Eel	0.20	Mushrooms	0.10
Herring roe	0.20	Okra	0.10
Salmon	0.20	Oranges	0.10
Soy sauce, dark, thick	0.20	Oysters	0.10
Macaroni	0.18	Parsnips	0.10
Peanut butter	0.17	Raisins	0.10
Parsley	0.15	Sweet potatoes	0.10
Sweetcorn on the cob	0.15	Watercress	0.10
Lamb	0.14	Yam	0.10
Beansprouts	0.13	Aubergines	0.05
Artichokes	0.12	Courgettes	0.05
Pearl barley	0.12	Tinned pineapple	0.05

Notes:

a The thiamine content is reduced to 0.05 on roasting.

· cashew and cauliflower soup ·
serves 4

This unusual soup is popular with children because of its mild, yet distinctive flavour. It's very simple to make.

---

1 small onion
1 medium potato
8 oz (225 g) cauliflower florets

109

1 oz (28 g) unsalted butter or polyunsaturated margarine
4 oz (112 g) shelled cashew pieces
1 pt (600 ml) vegetable stock
pinch ground nutmeg
½ teaspoon ground coriander
10 fl oz (300 ml) skimmed milk
sea salt
freshly ground black pepper

Garnish
fresh coriander leaves

Finely chop the onion. Peel the potato, keeping the peelings for vegetable stock, and dice into ¾ in (2 cm) cubes. Break the cauliflower into florets.

Melt the butter or margarine in a large saucepan, put in the onion and potato, cover and cook for several minutes until the onion is soft. Add the cashews and continue to cook, stirring, for 5 minutes. Add the cauliflower. Stir to coat with butter or margarine and cook for 1 minute. Add the stock, nutmeg and coriander. Cover, bring to the boil and simmer for 20 minutes.

Allow to cool slightly then transfer to a liquidizer and blend until smooth. Return to the pan, add the milk, season with salt and pepper and heat through.

Transfer to a soup tureen, garnish with fresh coriander leaves and serve immediately.

For extra thiamine
Serve with wholemeal bread or croutons.

· buckwheat salad ·
serves 4

This substantial salad has an unusual nutty flavour. I often serve it as a cold main course with baked or boiled potatoes and a range of other salads. It is also good with steamed sweet potato and other root vegetables such as swedes or carrots, or served with a pasta. You will find unroasted buckwheat in health shops.

---

8 oz (225 g) unroasted buckwheat
1½ pt (900 ml) boiling water
3 medium-sized tomatoes
4 oz (112 g) button mushrooms
3 tablespoons freshly chopped parsley
2 oz (56 g) shelled brazil nuts, chopped in half
sea salt
freshly ground black pepper

Dressing
4 tablespoons unrefined, cold-pressed olive oil
freshly squeezed juice of half a lemon
3 teaspoons tamari (soy sauce)
1 clove garlic, crushed

Put the buckwheat in a large saucepan, cover with boiling water, return to the boil, cover and simmer for 15 minutes, or until soft. Watch the water level as the liquid will gradually become absorbed. If any is left, drain and keep for vegetable stock. Put the buckwheat in a large salad bowl and leave to cool.

Mix the dressing before you cut any vegetables, to avoid loss of vitamins. Put all the ingredients in a screw-top jar and shake thoroughly.

Finely slice the tomatoes, wipe the mushrooms with damp kitchen paper, slice thinly, finely chop the parsley, then add the tomatoes, mushrooms, parsley and nuts to the buckwheat. Shake the dressing vigorously and mix in well with the salad. Season with salt and pepper. To enhance the flavour of the salad, you can leave it to marinate for a short while. Provided you coat it well with dressing, cover it and leave it in a dark place, there should not be too much loss of thiamine. Serve immediately.

For extra thiamine

Serve with baked potatoes and cauliflower and watercress salad with yoghurt dressing (see pp. 205, 244), a green salad or pasta salad (see p. 135). If you prefer hot vegetables, serve with steamed leeks, cauliflower or sprouts.

· *brazil nut roast* ·

serves 4–6

Most healthy eating books have a nut roast and this book is no exception. Now that vegetarianism is old hat and everyone knows vegetarians do not just live on nut roast, maybe it is time for it to make a come-back! Nut roast is best served with a sauce such as onion gravy (see p. 252) or salad.

---

6 oz (168 g) shelled brazil nuts, finely ground

6 oz (168 g) shelled cashew nuts, finely ground

1 clove garlic

1 medium onion

6 oz (168 g) button mushrooms

4 sticks celery

1 oz (28 g) unsalted butter or polyunsaturated margarine

2 tablespoons fresh parsley

2 oz (56 g) fresh wholemeal breadcrumbs

1 oz (28 g) wheatgerm

1 teaspoon tamari (soy sauce)

2 oz (56 g) Cheddar cheese, grated

freshly squeezed juice of half a lemon

1 teaspoon dried sage or 2 teaspoons freshly chopped sage

1 teaspoon dried thyme or 2 teaspoons freshly chopped thyme

1 teaspoon dried marjoram or 2 teaspoons freshly chopped marjoram

$\frac{1}{4}$ teaspoon cayenne pepper

2 free-range eggs, beaten

For the topping

1 oz (28 g) toasted sesame seeds

112

Garnish
freshly chopped parsley
lemon wedges

Preheat the oven to 190°C (375°F, Mark 5). To toast the sesame seeds, spread them on a baking sheet and place in the middle of the oven for twenty minutes, shaking occasionally.

Lightly grease a 2 lb (900 g) loaf tin. Put the nuts in a large mixing bowl.

Crush the garlic and finely chop the onion. Wipe the mushrooms with damp kitchen paper. Slice the mushrooms and celery finely. Heat the butter or margarine in a saucepan over a gentle heat. Add the garlic and onion, cover and cook gently for a few minutes. Now add the celery and mushrooms, cover again and cook gently until soft, then remove from the heat. Chop the parsley, make the breadcrumbs and add to the mixture with the ground nuts, wheatgerm, tamari, cheese, lemon juice, herbs, cayenne pepper and the beaten eggs, and mix well in.

Spoon the mixture into a 2 lb (900 g) loaf tin and spread evenly. Top with sesame seeds. Bake in the oven for 45 minutes until golden brown. Garnish with freshly chopped parsley and lemon wedges and serve immediately.

For extra thiamine
Serve hot with onion gravy (see p. 252), and baked potatoes with steamed sprouts, cauliflower or leeks; or stir-fry broccoli with ginger (see p. 181).

Serve cold with watercress salad (see p. 25), green salad or a selection of salads.

· *coconut rice* ·
serves 4–6

Coconut rice is a traditional Indonesian dish. It makes a delicious accompaniment to South-east Asian dishes such as chicken satay (see p. 150) and also goes well with many Chinese dishes such as pork and pineapple stir-fry (see p. 114).

Long-grain brown rice takes a long time to cook. Use brown basmati rice (available in health shops) if you prefer. Creamed coconut is available in Asian or Greek grocers and some super-markets.

---

12 oz (336 g) long-grain brown rice or brown
  basmati rice
3 oz (84 g) creamed coconut
1 pt (600 ml) boiling water
2 teaspoons turmeric
20 peppercorns, tied in muslin
sea salt
freshly ground black pepper

Garnish
fresh coriander leaves

Wash the rice under cold running water. Place in a large heavy-based pan or saucepan.

To make the coconut milk, grate the coconut into a measuring jug. Add the boiling water and stir until the coconut has dissolved, then add the coconut milk to the rice. Add the turmeric and peppercorns and mix in well. Bring to the boil, cover and simmer gently for about 15 minutes until the rice is soft, but still crunchy. If, towards the end, the rice appears to be sticking, add a little more boiling water and stir in well. Remove the peppercorns and transfer to a warmed serving dish. Garnish with fresh coriander and serve immediately.

· pork and pineapple stir-fry ·
serves 4

Lean pork lends itself very well to stir-frying because the speed of cooking means it retains its succulence and does not dry out. The best cuts of meat to stir-fry are pork steaks or fillet; or loin chops, with the fat and bone removed. Make sure the strips of meat are very thin, so they can cook through easily. Cut across the grain to tenderize. If you cannot find arrowroot in a health shop, use cornflour.

---

12 oz (336 g) lean pork
1 teaspoon arrowroot
2 tablespoons tamari (soy sauce)
2 tablespoons dry sherry
1 clove garlic
3 spring onions
1 fresh green chilli
1 green pepper
1 8 oz (225 g) tin pineapple pieces
1 tablespoon unrefined, cold-pressed corn (maize) oil
3 oz (84 g) beansprouts

Cut the pork into thin strips, about 2 in (5 cm) long, cutting across the grain.

Put the arrowroot in a medium-sized bowl and slowly mix in the tamari until the liquid is free of lumps, then stir in the sherry. Add the pork and mix well to coat. Cover with non-PVC cling film and leave to marinate for 15 minutes.

Just before you are ready to cook, crush the garlic. Cut the spring onions diagonally into 1 in (2.5 cm) lengths. Top and tail the chilli, slitting it down the sides and removing the seeds, and chop finely. Remove the top of the pepper and take out the seeds, but leave in the pith and core. Cut the pepper diagonally into thin strips, 2 in (5 cm) long. Drain the pineapples and retain the liquid for use elsewhere.

Heat the oil in a wok over medium heat. When it begins to smoke, add the garlic and chilli and stir-fry for 1 minute. Add the pork with its marinade and stir-fry until brown all over, then add the spring onions and green pepper and continue to stir-fry until the pork is cooked and reasonably firm. This will probably take about 5 minutes. Stir in the beansprouts and pineapple pieces and heat through thoroughly. Spoon the mixture into a warmed serving dish and serve immediately.

For extra thiamine
Serve with wholewheat noodles or with brown rice.

· blackeye bean curry ·
serves 4–6

A mild curry that stands well on its own or as one of a range of meat or vegetable curries. Do not be put off by its dark colour. To save time, cook the beans the night before and store in the fridge.

---

6 oz (168 g) blackeye beans
2 large onions
3 cloves garlic
2 medium green chillies
2 tablespoons unrefined, cold-pressed sunflower oil
1 teaspoon whole cumin seeds
1 teaspoon whole coriander seeds
1 teaspoon ground cumin
1 teaspoon ground coriander
1 teaspoon ground turmeric
8 oz (225 g) flat mushrooms
8 oz (225 b) cauliflower florets
1 lb (450 g) tomatoes
sea salt
freshly ground black pepper

Soak the beans overnight. Drain. Cover with boiling water, return to the boil and fast-boil, uncovered, for 10 minutes. Cover and simmer for a further 30–35 minutes until soft. (If using a pressure cooker, cover with fresh water, bring to the boil and simmer for 10–15 minutes.) Drain.

Finely chop the onions and crush the garlic. Top and tail the chillies, slitting them down the side and removing the seeds, and chop finely. Heat the oil in a large heavy-based pan. Add the whole cumin and coriander seeds and cook for a few seconds until they sizzle. Add the other spices and cook for 1 minute, stirring. Add the onions, garlic and chillies, cover and cook for 5 minutes. Meanwhile, wipe the mushrooms with damp kitchen paper and cut into $\frac{3}{4}$ in (2 cm) cubes. Break the cauliflower into small florets. Skin the tomatoes by plunging them in boiling water and leaving for 1 minute. The skins should then slide off easily. Keep the blanching water for stock. Chop the tomatoes into quarters.

Add the mushrooms, cover and cook for 5 more minutes. Add the cauliflower, tomatoes and beans, cover, bring to the boil and simmer for 10–15 minutes until the cauliflower is soft. The mushrooms should generate enough liquid to cook the vegetables and to prevent sticking. If you need to add more, use the tomato-blanching water. Season with salt and pepper and serve immediately.

For extra thiamine
Serve with brown rice, baked potatoes or wholewheat pasta; other curries such as spinach and lentil curry (see p. 60); yoghurt and cucumber dip (see p. 121) or a vegetable curry made with spinach, cauliflower, carrots, swede, turnips, sweet potato or aubergine.

· sean's fried rice ·
serves 4

This is a regular favourite in our household. It is a good way to use up left-over cooked rice and only takes a short time to prepare.

---

8 oz (225 g) short-grain brown rice
2 large leeks
8 oz (225 g) button mushrooms
1 oz (28 g) unsalted butter or polyunsaturated margarine
6 oz (168 g) unsmoked ham, chopped into $\frac{1}{2}$ in cubes
2–3 tablespoons tamari (soy sauce)
1 free-range egg

Put the rice in a large saucepan, cover with boiling water,

return to the boil, cover and simmer for 10–20 minutes, until soft but crunchy. Drain and rinse under cold water.

Thinly slice the leeks. Wipe the mushrooms with damp kitchen paper and slice thinly. Melt the butter or margarine in a large frying pan and add the leeks. Cover and cook for 5 minutes. Add the mushrooms, cover and cook for a further 5 minutes. Mix in the ham and the rice and heat through, stirring. Add the tamari and mix in well. When the rice is hot, break the egg into the pan and stir in until cooked. Serve immediately.

For extra thiamine
Serve with steamed vegetables such as courgettes or cauliflower or with stir-fried beansprouts.

· *brazil nut fruit surprise* ·
serves 4

The layers in this simple dessert always keep friends guessing. It is best served straight after preparation, otherwise it loses some of its texture. For contrasting flavour and colour, try other fruits such as strawberries or raspberries.

---

3 oz (84 g) shelled brazil nuts, roughly ground

1 oz (28 g) wheatgerm

2 oz (56 g) wholemeal breadcrumbs

8 oz (225 g) pitted prunes

1 pt (600 ml) boiling water

1 8 oz (225 g) tin pineapple pieces, drained and juice retained

1 15 oz (420 g) carton natural low-fat yoghurt

Preheat the oven to 180°C (350°F, Mark 4). To toast the brazil nuts, wheatgerm and breadcrumbs, mix them together and spread evenly on a baking sheet or a shallow ovenproof dish. Place in the middle of the oven and toast for 15–20 minutes until golden brown, shaking occasionally.

Put the prunes in a medium pan, cover with the boiling

water, cover, bring to the boil and simmer gently for 15–30 minutes until soft. (In my experience, the time prunes take to cook varies considerably, depending on how old they are and where you buy them from.) Watch the water levels and add more if they start to stick. Put the prunes in a liquidizer and blend to a smooth purée. Add the drained pineapple juice or more water if necessary. Spread the prune purée on the bottom of four wide glass bowls or large wine glasses, distributing it evenly between them. Using half the yoghurt, spread a layer on top of the fruit. Use half the nut mixture and spread a layer over the yoghurt. Keep eight pineapple pieces aside for the topping and put the rest on top of the nut mixture, then another layer of yoghurt and finish with a layer of nuts. Top with the pineapple pieces. Cover with non-PVC cling film and refrigerate for 15 minutes. Serve chilled.

Riboflavin

Sources of riboflavin (vitamin B₂)

Food	Mg per 100 g	Food	Mg per 100 g
Marmite (yeast extract)	11.00	Wheatgerm	0.72
Brewer's yeast	4.28*	Camembert cheese	0.60
Lamb's liver	3.30	Danish blue	0.60
Calf's liver	3.10	Alfalfa seeds	0.58**
Ox liver	3.10	Egg yolk	0.54
Pig's liver	3.00	Red chillies	0.51
Chicken liver	2.70	Aduki beans	0.50**
Ox kidney	2.10	Cheddar cheese	0.50
Lamb's kidney	1.80	Parmesan cheese	0.50
Coriander leaves, dried	1.50	Eggs	0.47
Chinese mushrooms, dried	1.32	Duck	0.45
Cod's roe	1.00	Egg white	0.43
Almonds	0.92	Edam cheese	0.40
Lamb's heart	0.90	Mushrooms	0.40

Food	Mg per 100 g	Food	Mg per 100 g
Caraway seeds	0.38	Mung beans	0.20
Sardines, canned in oil, fish only	0.36	No-pre-cook lasagne verdi	0.20a
Wheat bran	0.36	Oysters	0.20
Mackerel	0.35	Pistachio nuts	0.20
Cumin seeds	0.33	Skimmed milk	0.20
Fenugreek leaves	0.31	Spinach	0.20
Soya beans	0.31	Split peas	0.20
Sprats	0.31	Spring greens	0.20
Broccoli tops	0.30	Turnip tops	0.20
Dried peas	0.30	Broad beans	0.19
Eel	0.30	Cow's milk	0.19b
Parsley	0.30	Dried peaches	0.19
Pilchards, canned in tomato sauce	0.29	Millet flour	0.19
Lamb	0.28	Pumpkin seeds	0.19*
Soya flour	0.28	Herring	0.18
Natural yoghurt	0.26	Red kidney beans	0.18
Bacon	0.25	Salmon, canned	0.18
Pork	0.25	Soy sauce	0.17
Beef	0.24	Chicken	0.16
Calf's brain	0.24	Turkey	0.16
Lamb's brain	0.24	Brussels sprouts	0.15
Vine leaves	0.24	Buckwheat flour	0.15**
Sunflower seeds	0.23*	Chickpeas	0.15
Agar, dried	0.22	Crab, boiled	0.15
Blackeye beans	0.22	Peas	0.15
Chestnuts	0.22	Red pigeon peas	0.15
Rye	0.22*	Salmon	0.15
Rye flour	0.22	Wheat flakes	0.15**
Cashew nuts	0.20	Oats	0.14*
Dried apricots	0.20	Beansprouts	0.13
Dried prunes	0.20	Butter beans	0.13
Lentils	0.20	Haricot beans	0.13

Food	Mg per 100 g	Food	Mg per 100 g
Pecan nut	0.13*	Spring onion	0.11
Walnuts	0.13	Tuna, canned in oil	0.11
Brazil nuts	0.12	Wholemeal spaghetti	0.11
Single cream	0.12	Haddock	0.10
Bulgur wheat	0.11	Halibut	0.10
Feta cheese	0.11	Oatmeal	0.10
Octopus	0.11		

Notes:

a Information supplied by Record Pasta Ltd.

b This is the value for milk not exposed to light. There is a loss on exposure to sunlight of 10 per cent.

· yoghurt and cucumber dip (tzatziki) ·

serves 4–6

Tzatziki is served as a starter in Greece and Cyprus. It is also used, in a slightly different form, in Indian cuisine, to complement hot curries. If you like it rich and creamy, use Greek yoghurt. Add more garlic, lemon and mint to taste. Work quickly to avoid exposure to light.

1 15.9 oz (445 g) carton natural low-fat set yoghurt
three-quarters of a large cucumber
2 cloves garlic
1 tablespoon freshly chopped mint
2 tablespoons unrefined, cold-pressed olive oil
1 tablespoon freshly squeezed lemon juice
pinch of sea salt
freshly ground black pepper

Garnish
black olives
additional mint leaves

Put the yoghurt in a bowl and beat slightly to mix in the liquid. Chop the cucumber very finely, crush the garlic and finely chop the mint. Add to the yoghurt with the olive oil, lemon juice, salt and pepper. Mix in well. Cover with non-PVC cling film and chill.

Serve on individual plates, garnished with mint leaves, black olives and hot pitta bread.

· *mighty mushroom dip* ·
serves 4–6

This rich, creamy dip may be served with crudités such as celery, carrots or red peppers or used as a spread for sandwiches. Add alfalfa or beansprouts for extra texture.

---

1 lb (450 g) flat open-cap mushrooms
1 oz (28 g) unsalted butter or polyunsaturated
    margarine
$\frac{1}{4}$ teaspoon dried thyme or $\frac{1}{2}$ teaspoon freshly chopped thyme
3 tablespoons dry sherry or red wine (optional)
3 tablespoons fine oatmeal
sea salt
freshly ground black pepper
4 oz (112 g) low-fat cream cheese
4 tablespoons freshly chopped chives
freshly squeezed juice of half a lemon

Garnish
pumpkin seeds
slices of lemon

Wipe the mushrooms with damp kitchen paper and chop roughly. Melt the butter or margarine in a large pan, add the mushrooms and thyme, cover and cook for a few minutes until the mushrooms are just tender. Mix in the sherry, stir in the oatmeal and cook, stirring constantly, until the mushroom sauce thickens. Season with salt and pepper. Transfer the mushrooms to a blender and purée until smooth. Stir in the cheese, chives and lemon juice and mix them in well. Spoon into individual small bowls or ramekins, cover and chill until ready to serve. Sprinkle each portion with pumpkin seeds and garnish with a slice of lemon.

· almond and vegetable stir-fry ·
serves 4

You cannot beat a stir-fry for simplicity and speed, yet the end result is a delightful meal, impressive enough to serve to friends. Prepare all the vegetables in advance to enable you to work quickly but do not leave them exposed to light or air any longer than necessary. If your wok has a lid, use it where possible. You will find sesame oil in a health shop. 'Pure' sesame oil, in Chinese supermarkets, is usually refined and may contain additives.

---

2 tablespoons unrefined, cold-pressed sunflower oil
3 oz (84 g) whole shelled almonds, blanched
4 spring onions
2 sticks celery
4 oz (112 g) button mushrooms
4 oz (112 g) broccoli florets
4 oz (112 g) cauliflower florets
4 oz (112 g) mangetout peas
4 oz (112 g) spinach
2 cloves garlic
1 teaspoon fresh ginger, grated
4 oz (112 g) fresh beansprouts
freshly ground black pepper

For the sauce
1 teaspoon arrowroot
1 tablespoon dry sherry
2 teaspoons unrefined, cold-pressed sesame oil
2 tablespoons tamari (soy sauce)
5 fl oz (150 ml) vegetable stock

Make the sauce first, so you do not have to leave the vegetables out for too long.

Put the arrowroot in a small bowl and blend with a

little bit of water until you have a smooth paste. Add the sherry, oil and tamari then stir in the vegetable stock.

Heat half the sunflower oil in a wok or large frying pan. When it begins to smoke, reduce the heat, put in the almonds and quickly stir-fry until golden brown. Remove with a slotted spoon and drain on kitchen paper. Now prepare the vegetables as quickly as possible. Thinly slice the spring onions and celery diagonally. Wipe the mushrooms with damp kitchen paper and slice finely. Blanch the broccoli and cauliflower together by plunging in a large pan of boiling water and cooking for 1 minute. Drain, keeping the water for use in stock elsewhere. Top and tail the mangetout. Remove the stalks from the spinach, rinse and pat dry with kitchen paper. Chop coarsely. Crush the garlic and peel and grate the ginger. Heat the rest of the oil in the wok or frying pan. When it is hot, add the garlic and ginger and stir-fry for 30 seconds. Add the spring onions and celery and stir-fry for 1 minute. Add the mushrooms, mangetout and spinach and stir-fry until just tender. Mix the sherry sauce once again and add to the pan. Continue to stir-fry the vegetables until the sauce boils and begins to thicken. Add the cauliflower, broccoli, almonds and beansprouts and heat through. Season with pepper and serve immediately.

For extra riboflavin
Serve with wholewheat, egg or spinach noodles.

· *lamb and apricot stew* ·
serves 4–6

Neck or shoulder of lamb both work well in a stew but, if you do not like fat, it is worth buying a more expensive cut. If you are boning it yourself, you will need to allow at least 1 lb (450 g) extra. You need a fair bit of time for this stew. Serve with potatoes, rice or pasta.

124

2 lb (900 g) boneless lamb
1 large onion
½ in (1.3 cm) piece of fresh ginger
2 tablespoons unrefined, cold-pressed sunflower oil
1 teaspoon ground coriander
½ teaspoon ground cumin
1 teaspoon ground cinnamon
½ teaspoon grated nutmeg
8 cloves
1 cinnamon stick, 2 in (5 cm) long
8 oz (225 g) unsulphured dried apricots
sea salt
freshly ground black pepper
2 oz (56 g) shelled almonds, ground

Cut the lamb into 1 in (2.5 cm) cubes. Finely chop the onion, and peel and grate the ginger. Heat the oil in a large saucepan, add the onion and ginger, cover and cook until soft. Add the coriander, cumin, ground cinnamon and nutmeg, and cook for a minute or two, stirring. Add the lamb, stir in to coat with the spices, cover and cook for about 5 minutes until lightly browned. Cover the lamb with plenty of boiling water. Add the cloves and cinnamon stick. Return to the boil, cover and simmer gently for 30 minutes. If any fat rises to the surface, skim it off.

When the stew has been simmering for 30 minutes, put the apricots in a saucepan, with just enough boiling water to cover. Return to the boil, cover and simmer for 10 minutes or until just soft. Now put the apricots in a blender with any liquid that has not been absorbed and blend to a thick purée. Add this to the stew, cover and simmer very gently for a further 30 minutes, until the lamb is tender. Stir regularly to prevent sticking and add more water if necessary. Season with salt and pepper to taste.

Just before serving, remove the cloves and cinnamon stick. Stir in the ground almonds to thicken the sauce. Heat through thoroughly, stirring all the time to prevent sticking. Serve immediately with baked potatoes or brown rice.

For extra riboflavin
Serve with steamed spinach, broccoli, Brussels sprouts or spring greens or with spinach and lentil curry (see p. 60).

· *chestnut bake* ·
serves 4–6

Purist that I am, I used to struggle through peeling fresh chestnuts, but this is a complete waste of time, since much of the nut ends up clinging to the shell or gets eaten up on the way! Now I use dried chestnuts which are available all the year round in health shops.

Dried chestnuts need soaking overnight, but once soaked, they cook quickly. Serve with baked potatoes and salads.

---

8 oz (225 g) dried chestnuts
1 small onion
2 sticks celery
4 oz (112 g) button mushrooms
1 oz (28 g) unsalted butter or polyunsaturated margarine
2 oz (56 g) wholemeal breadcrumbs
2 oz (56 g) wheatgerm
2 tablespoons freshly chopped parsley
sea salt
freshly ground black pepper
10 fl oz (300 ml) cheese sauce (see p. 251)
$\frac{1}{4}$ teaspoon paprika

Soak the chestnuts overnight in cold water. Drain. Steam over a pan of boiling water, with a tight-fitting lid, for 20–30 minutes, until soft. Check halfway through that the water has not evaporated. Add more boiling water if necessary. Drain. Keep aside in the pan, with the lid on.

Preheat the oven to 190°C (375°F, Mark 5). Lightly

grease a medium-sized ovenproof dish. Finely chop the onion and thinly slice the celery. Wipe the mushrooms with damp kitchen paper and slice finely. Melt the butter or margarine in a large pan, put in the onion and celery. Cover and cook until soft. Meanwhile, mix together the breadcrumbs and wheatgerm in a small bowl. Add the mushrooms to the pan, cover and cook for a few more minutes. Chop the parsley and mix in. Add the chestnuts and heat through. Season with salt and pepper and spoon into an ovenproof dish.

Quickly make the cheese sauce (see p. 251), add the paprika and pour the sauce evenly over the chestnuts. Sprinkle the breadcrumbs and wheatgerm evenly over the top and bake in the middle of the oven for 20 minutes until brown and crisp on top. Serve immediately.

For extra riboflavin
Serve with a moist salad such as spinach and mushroom (see p. 180), or cauliflower and watercress with tangy dressing (see pp. 205, 241).

· *chicken liver bolognaise* ·
serves 4

Chicken livers are more digestible than lamb's or pig's liver, so they make a perfect, nutritious meal for children. You don't need large portions, because they are fairly rich. Make sure you do not overcook the chicken livers, or they will disintegrate. If you do not want to use wine, just double the amount of stock or use chicken stock. The sauce goes well with any pasta and rice or potatoes. It is inadvisable to freeze this dish.

---

1 lb (450 g) chicken livers, defrosted if frozen
2 oz (56 g) unsmoked back bacon
1 medium onion
2 cloves garlic
6 oz (168 g) button mushrooms

127

4 sticks celery

4 oz (112 g) carrots

1 oz (28 g) unsalted butter or polyunsaturated margarine

3 tablespoons tomato purée

5 fl oz (150 ml) red wine

5 fl oz (150 ml) vegetable stock

$\frac{1}{2}$ teaspoon dried oregano

$\frac{1}{4}$ teaspoon dried basil

2 bay leaves

sea salt

freshly ground black pepper

To serve

12 oz (336 g) wholemeal spaghetti

Trim the livers, removing any membranes, and chop into 2 in (5 cm) cubes. Remove the rind and fat from the bacon and cut into $\frac{1}{2}$ in (1.3 cm) cubes. Finely chop the onion and crush the garlic. Wipe the mushrooms with damp kitchen paper and slice finely. Finely slice the celery and the carrots.

Heat the butter or margarine in a heavy-based pan. Add the onion and garlic, cover and cook until soft. Add the mushrooms, celery and carrot, cover and cook for 3–4 more minutes. Add the bacon and chicken livers and cook, stirring occasionally, until the livers are well browned. Stir in the tomato purée and add the wine and stock. Add the herbs and bay leaves. Bring to the boil, cover and simmer gently for 20 minutes. Remove the bayleaf. Season with salt and pepper.

Start cooking the spaghetti, according to the instructions, in time to serve immediately. When it is just *al dente* (that is, tender but not too soft), drain and season with freshly ground black pepper. Serve with the bolognaise.

For extra riboflavin
Sprinkle with grated Parmesan.

· apricot delight ·

serves 4

This sugar-free dessert is really simple and quick to make. It is ideal for dinner parties or for home consumption.

---

8 oz (225 g) unsulphured dried apricots
10 oz (280 g) natural low-fat yoghurt
2 free-range egg whites
flaked almonds to decorate

Put the apricots in a pan and just cover with boiling water. Bring to the boil and simmer gently for about 20 minutes, until soft. Leave to cool in the pan, with the lid on. Drain, retaining the liquid for use. Put the apricots in a blender, with a little of the cooking water, and blend to a smooth purée. Stir in the yoghurt.

Separate the eggs. Cover and refrigerate the yolks for use elsewhere. Whisk the egg whites until stiff peaks form and gently fold into the apricot mixture. Spoon into individual glass bowls, cover and chill until required. Sprinkle with flaked almonds to serve.

· cashew and peach ice cream ·

serves 4

Making your own ice cream is great fun and is extremely simple. This one is always popular with children and adults alike. You will find natural vanilla essence in health shops.

---

4 oz (112 g) unsulphured dried peaches
4 oz (112 g) cashew pieces
5 fl oz (150 ml) skimmed milk
½ teaspoon natural vanilla essence
2 teaspoons clear honey
1 tablespoon unrefined, cold-pressed sunflower oil

For the topping
1 oz (28 g) extra cashew pieces, finely chopped

Put the peaches in a pan and just cover with boiling water. Return to the boil, cover and simmer for 20 minutes or until soft. Drain, keeping the liquid for use elsewhere. Put the peaches in a blender and blend to a thick purée. (Do not make the purée too smooth or else the ice cream will have no texture.)

Put 4 oz (112 g) cashews in a food processor or grinder and grind to a fine powder. Add the milk, vanilla essence, honey and oil and liquidize until very smooth. Add the peaches and blend a little bit more until you have a stiff, thickish purée. Transfer to a freezerproof container with an airtight lid. Freeze for 2 hours until firm. Scoop out into individual bowls. Sprinkle with the extra chopped cashews and serve immediately.

When using the ice cream on a separate occasion, I suggest you put it to soften in the refrigerator about 20 minutes before you want to eat it.

13

•

NICOTINIC ACID
(VITAMIN B$_3$)

•

Vitamin B$_3$ is also known as nicotinic acid and as niacin. In its active form, it is known as nicotinamide and niacinamide respectively.

Nicotinic acid, like riboflavin, works with certain enzymes in the production of energy from carbohydrates, fats and proteins. It is essential for maintaining healthy skin, tongue and digestive organs and is crucial to the proper functioning of the brain.

Vitamin B$_3$ and chromium are needed, along with three specific amino acids, to make the Glucose Tolerance Factor (GTF). This is a molecule that functions in the body to help maintain normal blood sugar levels.

Availability

The amount of vitamin B$_3$ available in foods depends on the form in which it is found. Most of the vitamin B$_3$ in wheat flour and corn products, such as cornflour, cornmeal and maize, is in a bound form that needs an alkaline environment in order to be released from food, and for absorption. Because bread, pastry and pasta dishes made with wheat flour use alkaline baking soda as a raising agent, most of the nicotinic acid in these foods is available to the body.

Vitamin B$_3$ can also be synthesized from the amino acid tryptophan, provided vitamin B$_6$ is present. This means that foods containing large amounts of tryptophan make a significant contribution to your vitamin B_3 status. The amount of vitamin B_3 in foods is usually expressed as nicotinic acid or niacin equivalents (see table on pp. 133–4), to take into account the contribution made by both nicotinic acid and tryptophan.

Signs of deficiency

Early signs of deficiency include: irritability, headaches, loss of memory and rapid mood swings. Skin changes such as redness, scaling and roughness occur. The tongue becomes sore and coated, with deep cracks. Gastro-intestinal complaints develop such as nausea, vomiting and diarrhoea.

The classical deficiency, which was common in the southern states of the USA in the early part of the twentieth century, produces pellagra, characterized by dermatitis, diarrhoea and dementia. This was probably caused by a high intake of corn products like maize, in which the nicotinic acid is present in a bound form.

Therapeutic uses

- Schizophrenia. Nicotinic acid has been used successfully to treat some schizophrenics. This has often been part of a megavitamin therapy programme.

- Blood cholesterol. Nicotinic acid, but not nicotinamide, has been used to lower blood cholesterol levels and the amounts of triglycerides, another group of blood fats that may be associated with heart disease.

- Chilblains. Nicotinic acid has been used with some success to treat chilblains. By causing the blood vessels to dilate, it improves blood circulation in the area.

LOSSES FROM FOOD

Vitamin B_3 is very stable to all cooking methods, but, as with the other B vitamins, the main losses occur through leaching out in cooking water and meat juices. These should be kept and used in stock or gravy.

Sources of nicotinic acid or niacin (vitamin B$_3$)

Food	Mg per 100 g expressed as nicotinic acid equivalents	Food	Mg per 100 g expressed as nicotinic acid equivalents
Marmite (yeast extract)	67.0	Coriander leaves, dried	10.7
Brewer's yeast	37.9*	Soya flour	10.6
Wheat bran	32.6	Lamb	10.4
Coffee, instant	24.9 a	Salmon	10.4
Peanuts	21.3	Pork	10.0
Peanut butter	19.9	Wholemeal spaghetti	9.9
Pig's liver	19.4	Wheatgerm	9.8
Lamb's liver	18.5	Beef	9.5
Ox liver	17.9	Duck	9.5
Tuna, canned in oil	17.2	Ox kidney	9.4
Calf's liver	16.7	Pasta verdi	9.0 b
Mustard seeds	16.7	Lamb's kidney	8.8
Grouse, roast	14.6	Parmesan cheese	8.6
Chicken liver	14.3	Bacon	8.5
Pigeon, roast	14.1	Bloater, grilled	8.4
Sardines, canned in oil, fish only	12.6	Halibut	8.3
Sesame seeds	12.6	Wholemeal flour	8.2
Rabbit	12.5	Pot barley	7.8
Pheasant, roast	12.1	Blackeye beans	7.7
Turkey	12.0	Octopus	7.6
Chicken	11.6	Indian tea	7.5
Mackerel	11.6	Sprats	7.5
Chinese mushrooms, dried	11.3	Herring	7.2
Pilchards, canned in tomato sauce	11.1	Haddock	7.1
Pig's kidney	11.0	Brown rice	6.8
Lamb's heart	10.9	Lemon sole	6.7
Salmon, canned	10.8	Split peas	6.7
		Eel	6.6

Food	Mg per 100 g expressed as nicotinic acid equivalents	Food	Mg per 100 g expressed as nicotinic acid equivalents
Saithe (coley)	6.6	Squid	5.3
Dried peas	6.5	Calf's brain	5.2
Plaice	6.5	Cod	4.9
Crab, boiled	6.3	Egg yolk	4.8
Danish blue cheese	6.3	Noodles	4.8
Camembert cheese	6.2	Pearl barley	4.8
Cheddar cheese	6.2	Tomato paste	4.8
Bulgur wheat	6.1	Almonds	4.7
Broad beans	6.0	Mushrooms	4.6
Stilton cheese	6.0	Buckwheat	4.5
Haricot beans	5.9	Brazil nuts	4.2
Edam cheese	5.8	Chickpeas	4.2
Lentils	5.8	Red pigeon peas	3.9
Butter beans	5.6	Anchovies	3.8
Dried peaches	5.6	Dried apricots	3.8
Spaghetti	5.6	Oatmeal	3.8
Wholemeal bread	5.6	Eggs	3.7
Mung beans	5.5	Rice flour	3.5
Red kidney beans	5.5	Peas	3.4
Macaroni	5.4	Hazelnuts	3.1
Sunflower seeds	5.4*	Frozen peas	3.0
Prawns	5.3	Rice, polished	3.0

Notes:
The figure is, where possible, for nicotinic acid (niacin) equivalents, which include the contribution made by tryptophan, an amino acid which can be converted in the body to nicotinic acid.

$$\text{mg nicotinic acid equivalents} = \frac{\text{mg tryptophan}}{60}$$

a Instant coffee can contain as much as 39 mg per 100 g. Decaffeinated instant coffee contains about the same amount.

b Information supplied by Pasta Foods Ltd.

· pasta salad ·

serves 4–6

This substantial salad can be served as a main course.

---

6 oz (168 g) wholewheat pasta shells
4 fl oz (120 ml) sweet and sour dressing (see p. 242)
6 oz (168 g) button mushrooms
1 medium red pepper
3 oz (84 g) tinned sweetcorn, preferably sugar-free
16 stuffed olives
2 oz (56 g) fresh beansprouts

Cook the pasta in lightly salted boiling water for 8–10 minutes, according to the instructions, until just soft. Meanwhile, make the dressing. Drain the pasta and, while it is still warm, mix with the dressing.

Wipe the mushrooms with damp kitchen roll and thinly slice. Remove the top from the pepper and take out the seeds. Leave the core and the pith. Cut into thin strips and then into ½ in (1.3 cm) lengths. Drain the corn, keeping the water for stock if it is sugar-free, and rinse under cold water to remove the starch. Drain the stuffed olives if in brine and rinse under cold water. Mix in the mushrooms, pepper, corn, olives and beansprouts with the pasta, making sure all the ingredients are thoroughly coated. Serve immediately.

· paella ·

serves 4–6

Paella needs no introduction. It is fairly time-consuming but the end result is always worth it. Use brown basmati rice if you are in a hurry and adjust the cooking time.

---

8 oz (225 g) frozen, cooked, peeled prawns, defrosted
4 boneless chicken breasts, about 4 oz (112 g) each
10 oz (280 g) long-grain brown rice
1 large Spanish onion

---

1 clove garlic
1 fresh red chilli
2 tablespoons unrefined, cold-pressed olive oil
2 14 oz (392 g) tins tomatoes
½ teaspoon paprika
¼ teaspoon cayenne pepper
1 pinch chilli powder
3 medium-sized courgettes
1 medium green pepper
4 oz (112 g) frozen peas
freshly ground black pepper

Defrost the prawns for at least two hours. Remove the skin from the chicken breasts and cut them into 1 in (2.5 cm) cubes. Wash the rice under cold water.

Finely chop the onion and crush the garlic. Top and tail the chilli, slit it down the side and remove the seeds. Slice finely. Heat the oil in a large, heavy-based pan and put in the onion, garlic and chilli. Cover and cook gently until soft. Add the chicken and cook for 5 minutes or until white all over. Add the tinned tomatoes including the juice (break them up with the back of a spoon), paprika, cayenne pepper, chilli powder, defrosted prawns and the rice. Cover, return to the boil and simmer gently for 20 minutes.

Finely slice the courgettes. Cut the top off the pepper and remove the seeds. Cut into strips, 1 in (2.5 cm) long. Add to the chicken with the frozen peas. Cover and simmer for a further 20 minutes, or until the rice is soft and the liquid has been absorbed. Stir regularly to prevent burning. Add water if necessary to keep the paella moist, but do not allow to go soggy. Season with pepper and serve immediately.

· tuna and pepper quiche ·
serves 4–6
An unusual, moist quiche that tastes good hot or cold.

---

1 7 oz (196 g) can tuna in oil

1 7 oz (196 g) can sweetcorn, preferably with no added
   sugar

4 spring onions

1 medium green pepper

1 fresh chilli

$\frac{1}{4}$ teaspoon chilli powder

3 free-range eggs

3 fl oz (90 ml) skimmed milk

3 fl oz (90 ml) soured cream

2 oz (56 g) Cheddar cheese, grated

For the crust

wholemeal shortcrust pastry made with 7 oz (200 g)
   flour (see p. 253)

Preheat the oven to 200°C (400°F, Mark 6). Lightly grease a
9 in (23 cm) flan case. Roll the pastry out thinly and use to
line the flan case. Flute the edges with a fork. Bake blind for
5–7 minutes to set the pastry. Reduce the heat to 190°C
(375°F, Mark 5).

Drain the tuna fish and flake into a bowl. Drain the
sweetcorn, rinse well and mix with the tuna fish. Finely chop
the spring onions, including the green part. Cut the top off
the pepper, remove the seeds and core, and chop finely. Top
and tail the chilli, slit it down the side and remove the seeds.
Chop finely. Add the spring onions, pepper, chilli and chilli
powder to the tuna and sweetcorn. Mix well together and
spread evenly over the flan case.

Beat together the eggs, milk and soured cream. Add the
grated cheese. Pour the liquid evenly over the tuna mixture.
Bake in the middle of the oven for 30–35 minutes until the
filling is set and golden brown. Serve hot or cold.

For extra nicotinic acid

Serve with steamed broccoli or peas and boiled potatoes.

• COUSCOUS •

serves 6–8

Couscous is a fiery North African dish with unlimited ingredients. If you can get hold of harissa, the hot chilli paste, it will make all the difference. You do not need a special couscousier or steamer to cook couscous. Simply place a sieve over the bubbling stew so the aroma can waft upwards through the grain. You can now buy pre-cooked couscous from most supermarkets. If you prefer lamb on the bone, buy at least 1 lb (450 g) more meat.

---

4 oz (112 g) chickpeas
3 oz (84 g) broad beans or peas
1 large onion
1 medium red chilli
½ teaspoon fresh root ginger
2 tablespoons unrefined, cold-pressed olive oil
2 lb (900 g) boneless lamb, cut into 1 in (2.5 cm) cubes
2 pts (1,200 ml) vegetable stock or water
1 14 oz (392 g) tin tomatoes
2 tablespoons tomato purée
¼ teaspoon cayenne pepper
1 teaspoon paprika
¼ teaspoon chilli powder
3 medium carrots
1 medium-sized swede
2 small turnips
4 medium-sized courgettes
2 oz (56 g) raisins
about 4 oz (112 g) couscous per person
4 tablespoons freshly chopped parsley
sea salt
freshly ground black pepper

Soak the chickpeas and the broad beans separately overnight. Drain. Finely chop the onion. Top and tail the chilli, slit it down the side and remove the seeds. Chop finely. Peel and grate the ginger. Heat the oil in a large heavy-based pan,

138

with high sides. (You have to use one that is tall enough to take a sieve over the top to steam the couscous. I usually use a pressure cooker.) Add the onion, chilli and ginger, cover and cook gently until soft. Add the meat and cook gently until browned all over. Add the stock, tinned tomatoes (breaking the latter up with the back of a spoon), tomato purée, cayenne pepper, paprika, chilli powder, chickpeas and broad beans; cover, bring to the boil and simmer gently for 30 minutes. Check the liquid level and add more stock if the stew looks as if it's going to stick.

Now prepare the vegetables. Thinly slice the carrots, peel the swede, keeping the peelings for stock, and cut into 1 in (2.5 cm) cubes. Cut the turnips into $\frac{3}{4}$ in (2 cm) cubes and thinly slice the courgettes. Add all the vegetables to the stew. Mix in the raisins. Return to the boil and simmer gently for a further 30 minutes, adding more liquid if necessary.

While the stew is cooking, prepare the couscous, to cook over it. Put the couscous in a large bowl, add a little bit of warm water and mix it in with your fingers to moisten the grain. Get rid of any lumps. Leave to swell for 10 minutes. Place the couscous in a large sieve, cover with a pan lid if possible and steam over the simmering stew, until the latter is ready.

Just before serving, chop the parsley and add to the stew. Season with salt and pepper to taste and add more spices if it is not hot enough for you. Serve out the couscous in large soup bowls. Place a ladleful of stew on top.

For extra nicotinic acid
Serve with fresh yoghurt spooned on top.

· chicken and almond in sweet and sour sauce ·
serves 4

A delicious blend of flavours makes this simple dish impressive enough to serve to friends. It is also quick enough to make after a day's work. Prepare all the ingredients just before cooking, so you can work quickly. The oils, arrowroot and tamari are available in health shops.

---

12 oz (336 g) boneless chicken breasts, skinned
2 teaspoons arrowroot
2 tablespoons dry sherry
1 free-range egg white, beaten
3½ fl oz (105 ml) sweet and sour sauce (see p. 252)
4 spring onions
2 cloves garlic
1 teaspoon fresh root ginger
1 green chilli
4 oz (112 g) mushrooms
1 medium-sized red pepper
1 7 oz (196 g) tin sweetcorn
2 tablespoons unrefined, cold-pressed corn (maize),
    safflower or sunflower oil
2 oz (56 g) whole shelled almonds, blanched
freshly ground black pepper

Cut the chicken into ½ in (1.3 cm) cubes. Put the arrowroot into a medium-sized mixing bowl. Gradually mix in the sherry to make a smooth paste. Beat in the egg white and mix in well. (You will not need the egg yolk.) Add the chicken pieces and toss in the marinade until thoroughly coated. Cover and refrigerate. Make the sweet and sour sauce before you prepare the other ingredients.

Now prepare the vegetables. Finely chop the spring onions, including the green part, crush the garlic, peel and grate the ginger. Remove the top of the chilli, slit it down the side, take out the seeds and finely chop. Wipe the mushrooms with damp kitchen paper and slice finely. Remove the top of the pepper and take out the seeds and the core. Cut diagonally into thin strips 1 in (2.5 cm) long. Drain the sweetcorn, keeping the water for stock, and rinse thoroughly under cold water.

Heat half the oil in a frying pan or wok over a high

heat. Add the almonds and cook quickly until golden brown. Remove from the pan with a slotted spoon and drain on kitchen paper. Take the chicken from the fridge. Heat the rest of the oil on high. When it is smoking, reduce the heat, add the spring onions, garlic, ginger and chilli and stir-fry quickly for a minute or two. Add the chicken pieces with the marinade, and stir-fry quickly to prevent sticking. Cook for about 2 minutes until it turns white. Add the mushrooms and pepper and stir-fry for another couple of minutes. Beat the sweet and sour sauce, then toss over the chicken and vegetables. Stir constantly until the sauce thickens, and coats everything. Stir in the sweetcorn and almonds and allow to heat through. Season with pepper to taste. Serve immediately.

For extra nicotinic acid
Serve with wholewheat or egg noodles or brown rice.

· *fig and apricot scones* ·
makes 8

Warm scones remind me of my childhood and what better for afternoon tea, served with home-made raspberry jam and butter or margarine. If you do not like the 'grittiness' of figs, use sultanas, dates or other dried fruit.

---

8 oz (225 g) wholemeal self-raising flour
pinch sea salt
3 oz (84 g) unsalted butter or polyunsaturated margarine
1 oz (28 g) raw muscovado sugar
1½ oz (42 g) unsulphured dried apricots
1½ oz (42 g) dried figs
4–5 fl oz (120–150 ml) skimmed milk

For brushing
extra skimmed milk

Preheat the oven to 220°C (425°F, Mark 7). Lightly grease a large baking sheet.

Put the flour and salt in a large mixing bowl. Add the butter or margarine in small pieces and, with your fingertips, rub it in until the mixture resembles fine wholemeal breadcrumbs. Add the sugar. Chop the fruit very finely (this is best done in a food processor), and mix in well, making sure you distribute it evenly because it tends to stick together. Add sufficient milk to make a soft manageable dough. Turn on to a lightly floured surface and knead lightly. Roll out to about ¾ in (2 cm) thick. Cut into rounds with a 3 in (7.5 cm) plain cutter.

When you have cut as many as you are able, roll the pastry back up into a ball, roll out the same thickness as before and cut the remaining scones. You may have to mould the last one by hand. Place close together on the baking tray, brush with milk on top and bake in the middle of the oven for 10–15 minutes until well risen and golden. Turn onto a wire rack and leave to cool slightly. Spread with butter or margarine and jam and eat immediately.

· rich fruit and nut cake ·

A filling cake that goes a long way. Unsulphured dried peaches and apricots are available in health shops.

---

2 oz (56 g) unsulphured dried peaches

3 oz (84 g) unsulphured dried apricots

2 oz (56 g) dried figs

3 oz (84 g) pitted dates

6 oz (168 g) shelled brazil nuts

2 oz (56 g) shelled walnuts

6 oz (168 g) butter or polyunsaturated margarine

3 oz (84 g) raw muscovado sugar

3 free-range eggs

1 tablespoon brandy

½ teaspoon natural vanilla essence

8 oz (225 g) plain wholemeal flour

1½ teaspoons baking powder
¼ teaspoon mixed spice
2 tablespoons skimmed milk

For the topping
1 oz (28 g) whole blanched almonds

Preheat the oven to 170°C (325°F, Mark 3) and lightly grease an 8 in (20 cm) cake tin.

Chop the fruit into ¼ in (6 mm) pieces and chop the brazil nuts and walnuts into similarly sized pieces. You can do all this in a food processor.

Cream together the butter or margarine and the sugar. Beat the eggs until they are light and fluffy, then mix into the butter (or margarine) and sugar with the brandy and the vanilla essence.

Mix together the flour, baking powder and mixed spice, then fold into the butter, sugar and eggs. Mix in well. Add enough milk to make the mixture light and creamy. Add the nuts and the fruit and mix in well. Transfer the mixture to the prepared cake tin. Spread evenly in the cake tin and level the surface. Distribute the blanched almonds evenly on top of the cake and press in lightly. Bake in the middle of the oven for about 1½ hours or until risen and golden. Transfer to a wire rack to cool. Store in an airtight container.

· *apricot upside-down pudding* ·
serves 6–8

Everybody likes a good pudding, especially if someone else has made it! It is quite rich, so you do not need huge portions.

---

12 oz (336 g) unsulphured dried apricots
2 oz (56 g) ground almonds
2 tablespoons water

For the sponge
4 oz (112 g) unsalted butter or polyunsaturated margarine
4 oz (112 g) raw muscovado sugar

¼ teaspoon natural almond essence
3 free-range eggs
6 oz (168 g) wholemeal self-raising flour
1 tablespoon skimmed milk (optional)
1 oz (28 g) flaked almonds to decorate

Just cover the apricots with boiling water, return to the boil, cover and cook for 10–15 minutes until soft. Keep an eye on the liquid and add a little more if it becomes absorbed. Put the apricots, with their liquid, in a blender and blend to a soft purée. Mix in the almonds and add a little water to keep the purée moist.

Preheat the oven to 190°C (375°F, Mark 5) and lightly grease an 11 × 7 in (28 × 18 cm) ovenproof dish. In a large bowl, cream together the butter or margarine and the sugar until light and fluffy. Mix in the almond essence. Add the eggs one at a time, and beat well after each addition. Fold in the flour and beat until you have a light, creamy mixture. Add a little milk if necessary. Spoon the apricot purée into the ovenproof dish and spread evenly over the base. Spoon the sponge mixture on top and spread evenly. Bake in the middle of the oven for 20–30 minutes until risen and golden. Run a knife round the edge of the baking dish, then turn the pudding out onto a flat, warmed serving dish. Decorate with flaked almonds. Serve immediately.

· peanut and banana loaf ·

This light loaf is quick and easy to make and is very popular with children. It has a bland but distinctive flavour and tastes good spread with butter or polyunsaturated margarine and sugar-free jam. Soya flour is available at health shops.

---

4 oz (112 g) plain wholemeal flour
4 oz (112 g) soya flour
2 teaspoons baking powder
½ teaspoon mixed spice
4 oz (112 g) shelled, unsalted peanuts, chopped

3 large bananas

2 fl oz (60 ml) clear honey

2 fl oz (60 ml) unrefined, cold-pressed peanut
(groundnut) oil

1 free-range egg, beaten

For the topping

1 oz (28 g) additional shelled, unsalted peanuts,
chopped finely

Preheat the oven to 190°C (375°F, Mark 5). Lightly grease a 2 lb (900 g) loaf tin.

Mix together the flours, baking powder, mixed spice and chopped peanuts in a large bowl. In a separate bowl, mash the banana and mix in the honey, oil and beaten egg. Add the wet ingredients to the dry. Beat well in.

Spoon into the loaf tin. Spread the mixture evenly and sprinkle the additional chopped peanuts over the top. Bake in the oven for 25–30 minutes until risen and golden brown. Leave to cool slightly, then transfer to a wire rack. Spread with butter or polyunsaturated margarine to serve.

Pantothenic Acid

Sources of pantothenic acid (vitamin B$_5$)

Food	Mg per 100 g	Food	Mg per 100 g
Dried yeast	11.0	Broad beans, boiled	3.8
Calf's liver	8.4	Ox kidney	3.1
Lamb's liver	8.2	Pig's kidney	3.0
Ox liver	8.1	Peanuts	2.7
Brewer's yeast	7.2**	Lamb's heart	2.5
Pig's liver	6.5	Ox heart	2.4
Chicken liver	6.1	Wheat bran	2.4
Egg yolk	4.6	Peanut butter	2.1
Lamb's kidney	4.3	Calf's brain	2.0

Sources of pantothenic acid (vitamin B_5)

Food	Mg per 100 g	Food	Mg per 100 g
Danish blue cheese	2.0	Oatmeal	1.0
Dried peas	2.0	Rye flour	1.0
Lamb's brain	2.0	Bloater, grilled	0.9
Mushrooms	2.0	Kipper, baked	0.9
Salmon	2.0	Sweet potato	0.9
Split peas	2.0	Walnuts	0.9
Soya beans	1.9**	Dried dates	0.8
Wheatgerm	1.9	Peas	0.8
Eggs	1.8	Plaice	0.8
Duck	1.6	Turkey	0.8
Soya flour	1.6	Wholemeal flour	0.8
Rye	1.5**	Beef	0.7
Watermelon	1.5	Dried apricots	0.7
Camembert cheese	1.4	Haricot beans	0.7
Lentils	1.4	Lamb	0.7
Lobster, boiled	1.4	Oats	0.7**
Buckwheat	1.2	Pot barley	0.7
Cashew nuts	1.2**	Cauliflower	0.6
Chicken	1.2	Crab, boiled	0.6
Hazelnuts	1.2	Rice, polished	0.6
Wheat	1.2**	Wholemeal bread	0.6
Wheat flakes	1.2**	Yams	0.6
Avocados	1.1	Almonds	0.5 a
Pork	1.1	Chestnuts	0.5
Tomato purée	1.1	Kidney beans	0.5
Broccoli tops	1.0	Oysters, raw	0.5
Butter beans	1.0	Pearl barley	0.5
Herring	1.0	Salmon, canned	0.5
Mackerel	1.0		

Note:
a On roasting, this is reduced to 0.25.

· chilled green pea soup with mint ·
serves 4–6

This soup has a naturally sweet flavour and is a refreshing green colour. It is ideal served cold on a balmy summer evening with piping hot garlic bread, straight from the oven.

---

1 small onion
1 medium potato
1 oz (28 g) unsalted butter or polyunsaturated margarine
1 pt (600 ml) vegetable stock
2 bay leaves
1 lb (450 g) frozen peas
3 tablespoons freshly chopped mint
sea salt
freshly ground black pepper
5 oz (140 g) natural low-fat yoghurt or 5 fl oz (150 ml)
    single cream (optional)

Garnish
fresh mint leaves

Finely chop the onion. Peel the potato, keeping the peelings for vegetable stock. Dice into $\frac{1}{2}$ in (1.3 cm) cubes. Melt the butter or margarine in a large saucepan. Add the onion and potatoes, cover and cook for a few minutes. Add the stock and the bay leaves. Cover, bring to the boil and simmer for 5 minutes. Add the peas, cover, return to the boil and simmer for a further 5 minutes. Chop the mint, add to the soup and simmer for another minute, then remove the bay leaves. Put the soup in a blender and liquidize until smooth. Season with salt and pepper. Transfer to a cold soup tureen, cover and chill. Just before serving, stir in the yoghurt or cream and garnish with fresh mint leaves.

For extra pantothenic acid
Serve with wholemeal garlic bread.

· peanut and blue cheese dip ·

serves 4

This is a crunchy dip that can be served with corn or tortilla chips, or with slices of celery, carrot or red pepper. It also makes a nutritious sandwich spread, especially if you add sprouted seeds such as alfalfa, lentils or mung beans. If you find Danish blue too strong, try different cheeses, for example, Sage Derby or another blue cheese.

---

4 oz (112 g) unsalted shelled peanuts

1 medium cooking apple

2 oz (56 g) Danish blue cheese, crumbled

1 oz (28 g) Cheddar cheese, grated

1 tablespoon unrefined, cold-pressed olive oil

1 tablespoon smooth peanut butter, sugar-free

freshly squeezed juice of 1 lemon

a few dashes hot sauce

Garnish

Sprigs of fresh parsley

Put the peanuts in a food processor and grind up as small as possible. Peel and core the apple, keeping the peelings for use in soup or stock. Chop into large cubes. Add the cheese, oil, peanut butter, apple, lemon juice and hot sauce to the peanuts and blend all the ingredients until smooth but crunchy. (If the dip is too crunchy for your taste, add a little more olive oil.)

Spoon into individual ramekins, cover and chill until ready for use. Garnish with fresh parsley to serve. Alternatively, place in a serving dish, cover and refrigerate. When ready to serve, garnish with fresh parsley and serve on individual small plates.

For extra pantothenic acid

Serve with hot wholemeal pitta bread or sticks of carrot, celery or green pepper. Or serve as a spread with cucumber, lettuce or tomato.

· stuffed mushrooms ·

serves 4

If you are fond of mushrooms, this is a great way to cook them. Stuffed mushrooms are filling enough for a main course, served with a selection of green salads, and potatoes or brown rice.

---

8 large flat mushrooms (about 3 in (7.5 cm) in diameter)
6 oz (168 g) button mushrooms
4 cloves garlic
4 tablespoons freshly chopped parsley
2 oz (56 g) unsalted butter or polyunsaturated
   sunflower margarine
4 oz (112 g) wheatgerm
4 oz (112 g) grated Parmesan
pinch of paprika
juice of 1 lemon
sea salt
freshly ground black pepper

Garnish
sprigs of fresh parsley

For serving
lettuce leaves, for example, Iceberg or Webb's Wonder

Preheat the oven to 220°C (425°F, Mark 7). Lightly grease a shallow baking dish.

Wipe all the mushrooms with damp kitchen paper. Separate the stalks from the caps of the flat mushrooms by gently moving them back and forth. Chop finely with the button mushrooms. Crush the garlic and finely chop the parsley.

Heat the butter or margarine in a large frying pan and add the mushroom stalks, button mushrooms, garlic and parsley. Cover and cook gently for about 5 minutes. Next, mix in the wheatgerm, grated Parmesan, paprika and lemon juice. Heat through thoroughly.

Season the flat mushrooms lightly on both sides with salt and pepper. Turn them gill side up. Divide the mixture

149

between the mushroom caps, pressing well into the gill surface of each, then place them in the baking dish and cover the dish with aluminium foil. Bake in the middle of the oven for 15 minutes. Serve on a bed of crunchy lettuce, garnished with sprigs of fresh parsley.

For extra pantothenic acid
Serve with brown rice and a range of salads, for example, spinach and mushroom, cauliflower and watercress, (see pp. 180, 205), or potato salad.

· *chicken satay* ·
serves 4

Satay is an Indonesian speciality served as a starter or main course with a fiery peanut dip. You can use pork, chicken or beef, or a mixture of all three. You need time in advance to leave the chicken marinating, but once the meat is ready on the skewers, it only takes a short time to cook. The peanut dip can be made another time and frozen. If you cannot find wooden skewers, use barbecue ones, available from a department store. You will find creamed coconut in some supermarkets and in Asian and Greek grocers.

---

4 boneless chicken breasts (about 4–5 oz, 112–140 g each)
1 medium onion
1 in (2.5 cm) piece fresh root ginger
4 teaspoons ground coriander
1 tablespoon raw dark brown sugar
1 tablespoon ground cumin
1 teaspoon ground turmeric
2 teaspoons aniseed
1 tablespoon unrefined, cold-pressed sunflower oil
1 oz (28 g) creamed coconut
5 tablespoons boiling water

For the chicken pieces
12 bamboo skewers (available in a Chinese
    supermarket)

For the peanut dip

7 oz (196 g) crunchy peanut butter, sugar-free (about
  two-thirds of a jar)

1 tablespoon unrefined, cold-pressed olive oil

4 tablespoons water

juice of 1 lemon or lime

1 small onion

2 cloves garlic

1 large green chilli

1 tablespoon tomato purée

$\frac{1}{4}$ teaspoon paprika

$\frac{1}{4}$ teaspoon chilli powder

Discard any skin from the chicken and cut into 1 in (2.5 cm) cubes.

To make the marinade, finely chop the onion and put it in a large bowl. Peel the ginger and grate it into the bowl. Add the coriander, sugar, cumin, turmeric, aniseed and oil and mix in well.

Grate the creamed coconut into a jug. Add 5 tablespoons of boiling water and allow to dissolve. Add this coconut milk to the marinade and mix well in, then put the chicken pieces in the marinade and keep turning them over until they are thoroughly coated. Cover and chill for 3–4 hours, turning the chicken several more times.

To make the peanut dip, spoon the peanut butter into a small bowl and beat in the olive oil and water until thoroughly mixed together. Squeeze the lemon or lime and add the juice to the bowl, mixing in well. Finely chop the onion and crush the garlic. Top and tail the chilli, slit it down the sides and remove the seeds. (If you want the dip very hot, leave them in.) Finely chop the chilli, then add the onion, garlic, chilli, tomato purée, paprika and chilli powder to the mixture. Stir all the ingredients well, cover and refrigerate until ready to serve.

Preheat the grill to medium. Thread the chicken on to the bamboo skewers, leaving a small gap in between each piece. Discard the marinade. Grill the satay sticks for 10–15 minutes, turning regularly. Serve the satay sticks on large plates. Serve the peanut dip in individual ramekins or on individual small plates.

For extra pantothenic acid
Serve with coconut rice (see p. 113).

· *mushroom and hazelnut flan* ·
serves 4

The nut cream in this flan makes a change from egg custard, normally used in quiches and flans, and means that non-dairy eaters can enjoy it too. The flan is best eaten hot with plenty of green salad. It is not recommended for freezing.

---

wholemeal shortcrust pastry made with 7 oz (200 g)
  flour (see p. 253)
6 oz (168 g) shelled hazelnuts
3 oz (84 g) shelled unsalted peanuts
3 oz (84 g) shelled cashews
10 fl oz (300 ml) water
1 tablespoon tamari (soy sauce)
½ teaspoon paprika
8 oz (225 g) button mushrooms
1 teaspoon unrefined, cold-pressed olive oil

Preheat the oven to 200°C (400°F, Mark 6). Roll the pastry out thinly and use to line a 9 in (23 cm) lightly greased flan case. Prick well in, flute the edges with a fork to decorate and bake blind for 5 minutes. Remove from the oven and reduce the heat to 190°C (375°F, Mark 5).

Grind half the hazelnuts with the peanuts and cashews in a food processor. To make the nut cream, add the water and blend until you have a smooth, creamy, thickish paste. Mix in the tamari and paprika.

Wipe the mushrooms with damp kitchen roll then slice finely. Heat the olive oil in a frying pan, put in the mushrooms, cover and cook for 5 minutes until soft. Add the remaining whole hazelnuts, cover and cook for a few more minutes. Spread the mushrooms and hazelnuts evenly over the flan case and pour the nut cream over them. Bake in the middle of the oven for 30–35 minutes until set.

For extra pantothenic acid
Serve with a green salad.

· *salmon steaks* ·
serves 4

Salmon is quite pricey but it compares favourably with meat, and there is no waste. It requires little effort or time to cook. Ask your fishmonger for advice about cut.

---

4 salmon steaks (6 oz (168 g) each), $\frac{1}{2}$ in (1.3 cm) thick
unsalted butter or polyunsaturated margarine
freshly squeezed juice of 1 lemon
4 bay leaves

Garnish
freshly chopped parsley
lemon pieces
freshly ground black pepper

Use the butter to grease lightly four pieces of greaseproof paper, large enough to wrap the salmon steaks in. Place one salmon steak on each sheet, squeeze the lemon juice over each one, add a bay leaf and wrap up tightly into a parcel. Place in a large saucepan and cover with boiling water. Return to the boil, cover and simmer gently for about 7 minutes. Remove from the water with a fish slice. Unwrap. Serve on a platter, garnished with freshly chopped parsley and pieces of lemon. Season with pepper to taste.

For extra pantothenic acid
Serve with brown rice or boiled potatoes and steamed carrots, parsnips, sprouts, peas or cauliflower.

153

· spiced lentils with rice (kitcheri) ·
serves 4

Kitcheri is an Indian dish comprising rice and pulses –
normally lentils or split peas – cooked together. In combination, they make an excellent form of protein. They can be
served on their own or as an accompaniment to meat or
vegetable curries. If you want to reduce the cooking time, use
brown basmati rice and omit the soaking.

---

6 oz (168 g) long-grain brown rice
6 oz (168 g) red lentils
1 clove garlic
2 medium green chillies
1 large onion
2 tablespoons unrefined, cold-pressed sunflower oil
$\frac{1}{2}$ teaspoon whole cumin seeds
$\frac{1}{2}$ teaspoon ground coriander
$\frac{1}{2}$ teaspoon garam masala
1 teaspoon turmeric
1 pt (600 ml) vegetable stock
sea salt

Garnish
fresh coriander leaves

Wash the rice and lentils under cold running water, then
leave to soak in fresh cold water for 30 minutes. Drain and
rinse.

Crush the garlic. Top and tail the chillies, slit the sides
and remove the seeds. Chop the chillies and onion finely.
Heat the oil in a heavy-based pan, add the onion, garlic and
spices and cook for a few minutes, stirring occasionally. Add
the chillies and cook for 1 more minute, then add the lentils,
rice and stock. Bring to the boil, cover and simmer gently for 35
minutes or until the rice is soft. Stir regularly and add more
water if necessary. (You need to keep a constant eye on the
water levels as, once the lentils absorb water, they tend to

start sticking.) Season with salt and serve immediately, garnished with fresh coriander leaves.

For extra pantothenic acid
Serve with steamed carrots, turnips or spinach.

· *watermelon wonder* ·
serves 6–8

Where I live, in North London, there is no such thing as a small watermelon! On Saturdays, you can see little children struggling home with a watermelon bigger than they are. Watermelons are usually sold whole or in large chunks. You can allow roughly half the weight for the skin, and 2 lb (900 g) of watermelon serves about eight people.

---

1 watermelon chunk, weighing about 4 lb (1,800 g), chilled
freshly squeezed juice of 1 lemon
2 teaspoons clear honey
4 oz (112 g) flaked almonds or pumpkin seeds to decorate

Scoop out the melon flesh with a melon baller about 1 in (2.5 cm) in diameter. As you go, remove the seeds. Place the melon balls in individual bowls. Squeeze the lemon juice into a small bowl and mix in the honey then sprinkle the lemon juice over the melon pieces. Decorate with flaked almonds or pumpkin seeds and serve immediately.

14

·

VITAMIN B₆

·

Vitamin B_6 in food comes in three closely related forms: pyridoxine, pyridoxal and pyridoxamine. With the help of magnesium and vitamin B_2, these compounds are converted, after absorption, into the biologically active form, pyridoxal-5-phosphate.

Vitamin B_6 is essential for life and is involved in over sixty enzymic reactions, including sugar metabolism and the breakdown of essential fatty acids. It is important in the metabolism of magnesium and some of its functions are dependent on zinc.

Vitamin B_6 plays a major part in the metabolism of amino acids from protein. It is essential for the production of vitamin B_3 from L-tryptophan, one of the three amino acids involved in the production of certain essential body chemicals that have a direct effect on the functioning of the brain and the nervous system. One of these chemicals, serotonin, is especially important in normal brain chemistry.

Signs of deficiency

Vitamin B_6 deficiency normally manifests itself first in mental changes including irritability, mild depression, nervousness and insomnia.

Physical signs usually appear later in the form of skin complaints rather like those that occur in B_2 deficiency: sore

156

tongue, bloatedness, water retention and, in severe cases, loss of appetite, weight loss, nerve damage, reduced resistance to infection and anaemia.

Vitamin B$_6$ deficiency tends to affect women more than men. Many women on the Pill, some pregnant women and some in the premenstrual phase of their cycle experience mild depression and sometimes mild diabetes. This may be because the high oestrogen levels that occur at these times interfere with the vitamin B$_6$ function that controls the serotonin levels in the brain. The control of mood is dependent on brain concentrations of serotonin and if serotonin levels drop, depression and sleep disturbances may occur.

Many other people are susceptible to vitamin B$_6$ deficiency including:

- Those on a high protein diet.
- Those taking medicinal drugs especially penicillamine, isoniazid and hydralazine.
- Diabetics.
- Hyperactive children and those with behavioural problems.
- People suffering from cardiovascular disease.
- Those allergic to food additives such as tartrazine.

Therapeutic uses

Many women suffering from premenstrual syndrome (PMS) have been helped by B$_6$ and magnesium, taken together. However, some women taking B$_6$ on its own have experienced toxic side-effects. Vitamin B$_6$ supplements should be taken with vitamin B complex. *Always consult your doctor before taking supplements.*

Vitamin B$_6$ may be of use in travel sickness, radiation sickness, morning sickness, kidney stones, skin allergies, acne and seborrhoeic dermatitis.

LOSSES IN FOOD

Vitamin B_6 is sensitive to both light and heat so some losses may occur during cooking. For example, between 30 and 50 per cent of vitamin B_6 may be destroyed while cooking meat. Vitamin B_6 is also leached out into cooking water and meat juices, so it is important to retain these for use in stock or gravy.

Sources of pyridoxine (vitamin B_6)

Food	Mg per 100 g	Food	Mg per 100 g
Wheatgerm	3.30	Turkey	0.46
Wheat bran	1.38	Bacon	0.45
Soya beans	1.20**	Herring	0.45
Oats	0.96**	Pork	0.45
Ox liver	0.83	Salmon, canned	0.45
Salmon	0.75	Red kidney beans	0.44
Walnuts	0.73	Tuna, canned in oil	0.44
Mackerel	0.70	Wheat	0.44**
Pig's liver	0.68	Plaice	0.43
Tomato purée	0.63	Avocados	0.42
Lentils	0.60	Chicken	0.42
Butter beans	0.58	Lamb's liver	0.42
Kipper, grilled	0.57	Buckwheat	0.40
Haricot beans	0.56	Chicken liver	0.40
Pot barley	0.56	Wheat flakes	0.40**
Hazelnuts	0.55	Crab, boiled	0.35
Calf's liver	0.54	Rye flour	0.35
Bananas	0.51	Shrimps	0.35
Mung beans	0.50	Duck	0.34
Peanut butter	0.50	Chestnuts	0.33
Peanuts	0.50	Cod	0.33
Plantain	0.50	Beef	0.32
Wholemeal flour	0.50	Ox kidney	0.32
Sardines in oil, fish only	0.48	Eel	0.30
Saithe (coley)	0.47	Egg yolk	0.30
Soya flour	0.46	Flageolet beans	0.30**

Food	Mg per 100 g	Food	Mg per 100 g
Lamb's kidney	0.30	Leeks	0.25
Raisins	0.30	Pig's kidney	0.25
Rice, polished	0.30	Potatoes	0.25
Sultanas	0.30	Dried prunes	0.24
Lamb's heart	0.29	Sweet potato	0.22
Rye	0.29 **	Broccoli tops	0.21
Brussels sprouts	0.28	Red cabbage	0.21
Kale	0.25 **	Camembert cheese	0.20
Lamb	0.25		

· date, banana and peanut salad ·

serves 4

An unusual, naturally sweet salad with a delightful contrast of textures. It is best served with a range of lighter salads because it is quite filling.

6 oz (168 g) pitted dates
4 tablespoons mayonnaise (see p. 247)
3 small bananas
6 oz (168 g) shelled unsalted peanuts

Chop the dates into $\frac{1}{2}$ in (1.3 cm) pieces and place in a salad bowl. Make the mayonnaise before you expose the bananas to the air. Peel the bananas and slice them thinly into the bowl. Mix in the peanuts. Add the mayonnaise and mix in well. Serve immediately.

· leek and potato soup ·

serves 4

This wholesome soup is perfect for a wintry evening. Do not overcook the potatoes otherwise they are liable to disintegrate, making the soup rather thick.

1 large onion
3 large leeks
12 oz (336 g) potatoes
1 oz (28 g) unsalted butter or margarine
1½ pt (900 ml) vegetable stock
sea salt
freshly ground black pepper
1 oz (28 g) pumpkin seeds

Finely chop the onion. Scrub the leeks and slice finely. Scrub the potatoes and only peel if the skins are really thick, keeping the peelings for stock. Dice into ½ in (1.3 cm) cubes.

Melt the butter or margarine in a large saucepan over a gentle heat. Put in the onion and leeks, cover and cook for 5 minutes until soft. Season with salt and pepper. Add the potatoes, cover and cook for a further 5 minutes, stirring occasionally to prevent sticking. Do not let the vegetables brown. Pour in the stock, bring to the boil, cover and simmer for 15 minutes or until the potatoes are soft. Transfer to a warmed soup tureen. Sprinkle with pumpkin seeds and serve hot.

· butter bean, tuna and green pepper salad ·

serves 4

This is a substantial, colourful salad that is very quick and easy to prepare. If you want to make it moister, add some tangy dressing (see p. 241). Cooking time for butter beans is very variable. They need to be soft but crunchy for a salad.

6 oz (168 g) butter beans
1 7 oz (196 g) tin tuna fish in oil
1 medium green pepper
2 spring onions
freshly squeezed juice of 1 lemon

160

Garnish
sprigs of fresh dill or parsley

Soak the butter beans overnight. Drain. Cover with boiling water, about double their volume, return to the boil and fast boil, uncovered, for 10 minutes. Reduce the heat and simmer gently for a further 25–40 minutes or until soft but crunchy. Add more water if necessary to prevent sticking. Drain and put the beans in a large salad bowl. (If using a pressure cooker, cover the beans with double their volume of water, bring to the boil and simmer for 10–15 minutes. Drain.) Drain the tuna of oil and flake into the salad bowl. Remove the top of the green pepper and take out the seeds, but not the core and pith. Cut the pepper into thin strips, about $\frac{3}{4}$ in (2 cm) long. Thinly slice the spring onions including the green part. Add the pepper, spring onions and lemon juice to the bowl and mix in well. Garnish with sprigs of fresh dill or parsley. Serve immediately.

· *celery, walnut and sultana salad* ·

serves 4

This light salad has a great combination of textures. It is ideal for summer or winter and goes well with bean loaves or flans.

3–4 tablespoons yoghurt dressing (see p. 244)
3 sticks celery
4 oz (112 g) shelled walnuts, chopped into quarters
4 oz (112 g) sultanas

Make the dressing before you cut the celery. Scrub the celery, thinly slice and place in a large salad bowl. Mix in the walnuts and sultanas. Add the yoghurt dressing and mix in well until the salad is thoroughly coated. Serve immediately.

· butter bean and leek flan ·
serves 4–6

A moist flan that is popular with children.

---

4 oz (112 g) butter beans
4 oz (112 g) button mushrooms
1 lb (450 g) leeks
2 oz (56 g) unsalted butter or polyunsaturated margarine
2 tablespoons fine oatmeal
1 14 oz (392 g) tin tomatoes
5 fl oz (150 ml) vegetable stock
1 tablespoon tomato purée
$\frac{1}{2}$ teaspoon dried basil or 1 teaspoon freshly chopped basil
$\frac{1}{2}$ teaspoon dried marjoram or 1 teaspoon freshly chopped
  marjoram
freshly ground black pepper
2–4 oz (56–112 g) Cheddar cheese

For the flan crust
wholemeal shortcrust pastry, made with
  7 oz (196 g) flour (see p. 253)

Soak the butter beans overnight. Drain and rinse. Put in a pan and cover with boiling water. Return to the boil and fast-boil, uncovered, for at least 10 minutes. Reduce the heat and simmer for a further 25–40 minutes, until soft. Keep an eye on the water level and add more if necessary to prevent sticking. (If using a pressure cooker, cover with fresh water, bring to the boil and simmer for 10–15 minutes.) Drain.

Preheat the oven to 200°C (400°F, Mark 6). Roll the pastry out thinly and use to line a 9 in (23 cm) flan dish. Crimp the edges with a fork to decorate. Bake blind for 5–7 minutes, to set the pastry. Remove from the oven and reduce the heat to 190°C (375°F, Mark 5).

Wipe the mushrooms with damp kitchen paper and slice finely. Scrub the leeks and cut into slices $\frac{1}{2}$ in (1.3 cm) wide. Melt the butter or margarine in a large saucepan or frying pan. Add the mushrooms, cover and cook for a few minutes. Add the leeks, cover and cook for a further 10 minutes.

162

Sprinkle the oatmeal over the vegetables and mix it in well with the fat so it does not stick, then immediately add the tinned tomatoes with their juice (breaking them up with the back of a spoon), then the stock. Bring to the boil and simmer for several minutes, stirring regularly until the mixture thickens. Mix in the tomato purée, butter beans and herbs. Heat through and season with pepper. Pour the mixture into the flan dish and sprinkle with grated cheese. Bake for 20–25 minutes until golden brown. Serve hot.

For extra B$_6$
Serve with baked potatoes and steamed cauliflower or broccoli, topped with toasted sesame seeds.

· *mackerel fish cakes* ·
makes about 8 fish cakes

Fish cakes are a great way to make fish more palatable for children. Tinned mackerel are very convenient and they contain no additives. These fish cakes are quite moist but if you want to serve them with a sauce, try the simple tomato sauce recipe on p. 249.

---

12 oz (336) potatoes
2 4 oz (112 g) tins mackerel in tomato sauce
2 tablespoons freshly chopped spring onion
3 tablespoons freshly squeezed lemon juice
1 tablespoon tomato purée
freshly ground black pepper
1 teaspoon dried oregano
1 tablespoon wholewheat flour
1 free-range egg, beaten
2–3 oz (56–84 g) jumbo oats

Peel the potatoes, keeping the peelings for stock, cover with boiling water and simmer for about 20 minutes until soft.

Flake the fish into a large bowl, with the tomato sauce.

Finely dice the spring onion, including the green bits. Squeeze the lemon juice. Add the onion, lemon juice, tomato purée, pepper and oregano and mix in well with the fish. Drain the potatoes, retaining the liquid for use elsewhere. Mash and mix well in with the fish.

With lightly floured hands, shape the mixture into 8 rounds. Brush each fish cake with beaten egg on both sides. Spread the oats on a clean surface and coat the fish cakes on both sides, pressing well in. Put the fish cakes on a plate, cover and chill for 30 minutes. Preheat the grill to moderate. Grill the fish cakes for 15 minutes, turning once.

For extra B$_6$
Serve with brown rice and steamed vegetables such as leeks, kale, carrots or sweet potato.

· *haricot bean and aubergine casserole* ·
serves 4–6

Serve this casserole with wholewheat macaroni or pasta shells to form a complete protein. To reduce cooking time, you can cook the beans the day before and store them in the fridge.

---

4 oz (112 g) haricot beans
2 medium-sized aubergines
1 medium onion
2 cloves garlic
2 tablespoons unrefined, cold-pressed olive oil
2 14 oz (392 g) tins tomatoes
1 teaspoon dried thyme or 2 teaspoons freshly chopped thyme
2 tablespoons tomato purée
2 tablespoons freshly chopped parsley
1 teaspoon dried marjoram or 2 teaspoons freshly chopped marjoram
freshly ground black pepper
5 oz (140 g) natural low-fat yoghurt
4 oz (112 g) low-fat cottage cheese
2 oz (56 g) grated Parmesan

Soak the beans overnight.

Cut the aubergines into slices $\frac{1}{2}$ in (1.3 cm) thick. Place in the drum of a salad-spinner or a colander and sprinkle with salt. Cover, put in the fridge and leave to drain for about 30 minutes. Rinse with cold water and spin dry or pat dry with kitchen paper. Meanwhile, drain the beans. Put in a pan and cover with boiling water. Return to the boil and fast-boil, uncovered, for 10 minutes. Remove any scum that might appear. Simmer for a further 40–50 minutes. (If using a pressure cooker, cover with fresh water, bring to the boil and simmer for about 20 minutes.) Drain.

Finely chop the onion, crush the garlic and dice the aubergines into $\frac{1}{2}$ in (1.3 cm) cubes. Heat the olive oil in a large heavy-based pan or casserole. Put in the onions and garlic and cook gently until soft. Add the aubergines and cook for a further 2 minutes, stirring. Add the tomatoes with their juice (breaking them up with the back of a spoon). Cover, bring to the boil and simmer for 5 minutes. Add the beans, thyme and tomato purée, cover and simmer gently for 20 minutes, stirring occasionally to prevent sticking. Add a little water if necessary. Chop the parsley. Add the parsley and marjoram to the casserole and season with pepper. Mix together the yoghurt and cottage cheese. Stir into the casserole and heat through. Just before serving, sprinkle with Parmesan. Serve immediately.

For extra B$_6$

Serve with pot barley or brown rice and extra vegetables such as steamed cauliflower, broccoli, sprouts or peas, and sprinkle with extra Parmesan cheese.

· lentil bake ·
serves 4

A smooth, mild-flavoured dish that is very popular with children. Try hazelnuts for a different flavour.

1½ lb (675 g) potatoes
1 medium-sized onion
2 large leeks
2 oz (56 g) unsalted butter or polyunsaturated margarine
6 oz (168 g) carrots
10 oz (280 g) cauliflower florets
½ teaspoon dried thyme or 1 teaspoon freshly chopped thyme
2 bay leaves
1 bouquet garni
8 oz (225 g) red lentils
4 oz (112 g) shelled walnuts, coarsely chopped
sea salt
freshly ground black pepper

For the topping
extra chopped walnuts

Garnish
sprigs of fresh parsley

Peel the potatoes, keeping the peelings for stock. Put them in a pan, cover with boiling water, return to the boil, cover and simmer for about 20 minutes or until just soft. Drain, retaining the liquid for stock. Do not mash until the last minute. Meanwhile, finely chop the onion and slice the leeks finely. Melt the butter in a large frying pan, add the onion and leeks, cover and cook for about 5 minutes or until soft. Finely dice the carrots and break the cauliflower florets into ½ in (1.3 cm) pieces. Add to the frying pan, with the thyme, bay leaves and bouquet garni. Cover and cook gently for about 15 minutes or until the carrots and cauliflower are just tender.

Pick over the lentils and remove any chaff. Put in another pan, cover with boiling water, return to the boil and skim off any scum. Cover and simmer for about 10 minutes, until just soft. Drain. Preheat the oven to 200°C (400°F, Mark 6). Lightly grease a medium-sized shallow ovenproof dish.

Remove the bay leaves and the bouquet garni from the

vegetables, then add the lentils and the walnuts and mix in well. Season with salt and pepper to taste. Spoon the mixture into the ovenproof dish and spread evenly. Mash the potatoes and spread over the top. Press in with a fork, to make a ridged pattern. Bake for about 20 minutes until golden brown. Top with chopped walnuts and garnish with sprigs of parsley. Serve hot.

For extra B$_6$
Serve with steamed vegetables such as Brussels sprouts, kale, broccoli, spinach or spring greens.

· baked bananas ·
serves 4
An exotic yet simple dessert for all occasions.

---

4 large bananas
freshly squeezed juice of half a lemon
2–3 teaspoons clear honey
2 tablespoons brandy (optional)
2 oz (56 g) shelled walnuts, chopped
5 oz (140 g) Greek yoghurt (about half a carton)

Preheat the oven to 180°C (350°F, Mark 4).

Place the bananas in their skins, just as they are, on a baking sheet and bake for 15 minutes. The skins will go black but this does not mean they are burned. Mix together the lemon juice and the honey in a small dish and add the brandy, if you are using it. Carefully slit the bananas right along both sides to the top and slide them out on to individual plates. Sprinkle with the lemon juice mixture and chopped nuts. Serve immediately with Greek yoghurt.

· banana and walnut cake ·
This cake has a mild, but distinctive flavour, but it is not too

heavy. It is very popular with children and is usually a great success at their parties.

---

4 oz (112 g) unsalted butter or polyunsaturated margarine
4 oz (112 g) raw dark muscovado sugar
2 free-range eggs
4 oz (112 g) wholemeal self-raising flour
1 oz (28 g) wheatgerm
3 medium bananas, peeled
4 oz (112 g) shelled walnuts

Preheat the oven to 190°C (375°F, Mark 5). Lightly grease an 8 in (20 cm) cake tin.

Cream together the butter or margarine and the sugar until light and fluffy. Beat in the eggs, one at a time. Fold in the flour and the wheatgerm. Mash the bananas and beat well into the mixture. Finely chop the walnuts and mix well in. Spoon the mixture into the prepared cake tin and spread it evenly. Bake in the oven for 25–30 minutes or until a skewer comes out clean. Cool slightly in the tin then transfer to a wire rack. Store in an airtight container.

15

•

VITAMIN B$_{12}$

•

Vitamin B$_{12}$ is essential for maintaining a healthy nervous system and it helps to form the myelin sheath that insulates the nerve-fibres. It is necessary for the production of red blood cells that carry oxygen round the body and is required for the synthesis of DNA, which is the basis of body cell production.

Vitamin B$_{12}$ is absorbed by the small intestine. This process requires the presence of the 'intrinsic factor', a compound normally produced by the stomach, which combines with vitamin B$_{12}$ allowing it to be absorbed. It is then transported to the liver where it may be stored for several years.

Signs of deficiency

Vitamin B$_{12}$ deficiency is caused by malabsorption into the blood, leading to pernicious anaemia. Symptoms include: exhaustion, shortness of breath and pale skin. Because B$_{12}$ is stored for several years, however, a deficiency may not appear for a long time. Malabsorption of B$_{12}$ eventually leads to degeneration of the nerve-fibres in the spinal cord and elsewhere. This causes numbness and tingling in the hands and feet, clumsiness and difficulty with walking.

Vitamin B$_{12}$ deficiency also affects mental function, causing confusion, depression, listlessness and tremors. Other symptoms include: smooth, sore tongue and menstrual disorders.

THOSE MOST AT RISK OF DEFICIENCY

Because the body stores most of the vitamin absorbed, requirements are minimal. However, some people are more susceptible to deficiency. These include:

- vegans.

- anyone with pernicious anaemia or other diseases involving impaired absorption of B_{12}.

- those on some medicinal drugs used to cure duodenal or peptic ulcers.

Therapeutic uses

Vitamin B_{12} may be of use to people with mild mental problems, especially elderly people; and to those with muscle fatigue.

Vitamin B_{12} and folic acid are often prescribed together for pregnant women, because of the extra demands of the developing foetus.

LOSSES FROM FOOD

Vitamin B_{12} is remarkably stable no matter which cooking method is used and because it is present in such tiny quantities, leaching out does not normally occur.

Sources of vitamin B_{12}

Vitamin B_{12} is normally found only in animal-based foods, but it is also found in small quantities in some sea vegetables; in spirulina, a form of algae; sprouted beans, miso and soy sauce.

Food Microgram per 100 g		Food	Microgram per 100 g
Ox liver	110.0	Sardines, canned in oil, fish only	28.0
Calf's liver	100.0	Pig's liver	25.0
Lamb's liver	84.0	Oysters	15.0
Chicken liver	56.0	Pig's kidney	15.0
Lamb's kidney	55.0	Ox heart	13.0
Ox kidney	31.0		

Food	Microgram per 100 g	Food	Microgram per 100 g
Pilchards, canned in tomato sauce	12.0	Shrimps, frozen, shell removed	2.6
Anchovies	11.0	Beef	2.0
Bloater, grilled	11.0	Cod	2.0
Kipper, baked	11.0	Lamb	2.0
Cod's roe	10.0	Plaice	2.0
Rabbit	10.0	Turkey	2.0
Mackerel	10.0	Eggs	1.8a
Calf's brain	9.0	Cheddar cheese	1.5
Lamb's brain	9.0	Parmesan cheese	1.5
Bovril	8.3	Edam cheese	1.4
Lamb's heart	8.0	Feta cheese	1.4
Liver sausage	8.0	Squid	1.3
Lamb's tongue	7.0	Camembert cheese	1.2
Herring	6.0	Danish blue cheese	1.2
Herring roe	5.0	Eel	1.0
Salmon	5.0	Haddock	1.0
Tuna, canned in oil	5.0	Halibut	1.0
Egg yolk	4.9	Lemon sole	1.0
Saithe (coley)	4.0	Lobster, boiled	1.0
Salmon, canned	4.0	Cottage cheese	0.5
Duck	3.0	Marmite (yeast extract)	0.5
Pork	3.0	Cow's milk	0.3
Free-range eggs	2.9	Single cream	0.2

Note: a This value is for battery eggs. Free-range eggs contain 2.9.

· smoked mackerel pâté ·

serves 4–6

Smoked mackerel is extremely rich, so a little of this moist pâté goes a long way. It is also very salty so I suggest you remove the salt by the jugging method outlined below. Ask your fishmonger for undyed smoked mackerel or those dyed with natural colouring, if possible. You can buy smetana in health shops and some supermarkets.

171

2 small smoked mackerel fillets
8 oz (225 g) low-fat cottage cheese, additive-free
2 fl oz (60 ml) soured cream or smetana
freshly squeezed juice of half a lemon

Garnish
freshly chopped parsley or dill weed

To remove the salt, put the smoked mackerel in a jug and pour boiling water over them. Leave for 5 minutes, then pour away the water. Repeat the process. Drain.

Skin the mackerel, remove any bones and flake the flesh finely into a bowl. Mix in the cottage cheese, soured cream (or smetana) and lemon juice. Cover and chill. Garnish with freshly chopped parsley or dill weed and serve on individual plates with hot wholemeal pitta bread or toast. Or serve with crudités such as carrot, celery or fennel.

· chicken liver and orange pâté ·

serves 4

This is a smooth, light pâté, that is quick and easy to make. It is inadvisable to refreeze chicken livers, once defrosted.

1 lb (450 g) chicken livers, defrosted, if used from
   frozen
4 spring onions
1 clove garlic, crushed
2 tablespoons unrefined, cold-pressed olive oil
finely grated rind of 1 orange
juice of 1 orange, freshly squeezed
2 fl oz (60 ml) vegetable stock
1 teaspoon dried sage
2 tablespoons fine oatmeal
4 oz (112 g) low-fat cottage cheese, additive-free
freshly ground black pepper

Pick over the livers and trim off any dark patches or white membranes. Rinse and pat dry with kitchen paper. Finely chop the spring onions and crush the garlic. Heat the oil in a frying pan and quickly sauté the onions and garlic. Reduce the heat and add the chicken livers. Cook gently until browned all over. Add the orange rind, juice, stock and sage. Cover and simmer for 5 minutes. Add the oatmeal, stirring the mixture until it thickens. Cool slightly, then place the mixture in a blender. Add the cottage cheese and purée until smooth. Season with pepper. Spoon into individual ramekins and spread evenly. Cover with non-PVC cling film and refrigerate until ready to serve. Garnish each portion with an orange slice and serve with wholemeal toast or warm wholemeal pitta bread.

· cod in hot sauce ·

serves 4

The fiery sauce lends a Caribbean touch to this quick dish. Serve with brown rice, wholemeal pasta or potatoes.

---

4 cod fillets, skinned, weighing about 6 oz (168 g) each
¼ teaspoon cayenne pepper
4 cloves garlic
1 large onion
2 fresh red chillies
2 tablespoons unrefined, cold-pressed olive oil
1 lb (450 g) tomatoes
2 fresh red peppers
¼ teaspoon chilli powder
2 teaspoons ground cumin
2 tablespoons tomato purée
15 fl oz (450 ml) boiling water
sea salt
freshly ground black pepper

Garnish
fresh coriander leaves

173

Rinse the fish under cold water and pat dry with kitchen paper. Sprinkle lightly on both sides with cayenne pepper. Crush 2 of the garlic cloves and spread over both sides of the fish.

Crush the other 2 garlic cloves. Top and tail the chillies, slit each down the side and remove the seeds. (If you want the dish very hot, leave them in.) Finely chop the chillies and onion. Heat the oil in a large heavy-based pan. Put in the garlic, onion and chillies, cover and cook gently for about 5 minutes.

Now skin the tomatoes. Put them in a bowl and cover with boiling water. Leave to stand for 1 minute, then pull off the skins. Chop into ¾ in (2 cm) cubes. Remove the top from the red peppers, take out the seeds and the core. Leave in the pith. Slice into thin strips, about 1 in (2.5 cm) long. Stir the chilli powder, cumin, tomatoes and peppers into the pan. Cover and simmer gently for about 10 minutes until the tomatoes are mushy. Stir in the tomato purée, add the boiling water and put in the fish. Bring to the boil, cover and simmer gently for 15–20 minutes or until the fish is soft. Do not let it overcook, otherwise it will disintegrate. Season with salt and pepper. Transfer to a large warmed serving dish. Garnish with fresh coriander and serve immediately.

· squid in red wine ·
serves 4–6

This dish is based on Jane Grigson's recipe. Baby squid are more often available than large squid, but they take a bit more time to prepare. The weight below is for uncleaned squid. Once you have prepared them, the fish will weigh much less. Although the amount left may look meagre, you will probably find the quantities sufficient, because squid is very rich. I usually serve this with plenty of wholemeal pasta. It also goes well with boiled or baked potatoes or brown rice.

3 lb (1,350 g) squid
1 large onion

1 clove garlic

2 tablespoons unrefined, cold-pressed olive oil

1 14 oz (392 g) tin tomatoes

2 tablespoons tomato purée

10 fl oz (300 ml) red wine

$\frac{1}{4}$ teaspoon raw muscovado sugar

$\frac{1}{4}$ teaspoon paprika

$\frac{1}{2}$ teaspoon dried thyme or 1 teaspoon freshly chopped thyme

1 teaspoon dried marjoram or 2 teaspoons freshly chopped marjoram

sea salt

freshly ground black pepper

4 tablespoons freshly chopped parsley

Prepare the squid as follows: grasp the tentacles that are hanging from the bag, and pull out. The head and innards will slip out. Run your finger over the squid, from the closed end, to ensure that all the innards have come out. Cut the tentacles from the head and put aside.

Attached to the head, you will see a long narrow ink sac. (You will see the ink through the transparent membrane.) If you need it for a recipe, which you do not here, carefully detach it from the head and put it in a bowl. Discard the head. Inside the bag, you will find a quill that looks like a piece of plastic. Pull it out and discard. You should now be left with the bag part of the fish, including the fins. Rinse the bag and tentacles under running water, rubbing off the pink outer membrane of the bag. Pat dry with kitchen paper. Cut the bag into thin rings and the tentacles into $\frac{3}{4}$ in (2 cm) pieces.

Finely chop the onion and crush the garlic. Heat the oil in a large heavy-based pan, put in the onion and the garlic, cover and cook gently for 5 minutes. Add the squid, cover and cook for about 10 minutes, until lightly browned, stirring regularly. In fact, the squid will be pinkish brown. Add the tinned tomatoes (breaking them up with the back of a spoon), the tomato purée, wine, sugar, paprika and thyme. Cover, bring to the boil and simmer gently for 15–30 minutes, until the squid is tender. Mix in the marjoram. Season with salt and pepper. Chop the parsley. Serve the squid immediately and sprinkle the chopped parsley over the top.

16

·

FOLIC ACID

·

Folic acid is closely linked to vitamin B_{12} in some of its functions, for example, it works with B_{12} to produce haemoglobin, the pigment in red blood cells that carries oxygen round the body.

Like B_{12}, it is essential for maintaining a healthy nervous system and it contributes to the production of certain body chemicals that are important to brain function.

Folic acid is essential for the production of RNA and DNA, which form the basis of our genetic make-up. It is particularly important for the growth of the developing foetus and the development of its immune system.

Folic acid is absorbed from the first part of the small intestine and transported to the liver where it is stored for several months.

Signs of deficiency

Lack of folic acid causes megoblastic anaemia, where the red blood cells become irregular in size and shape. They have a much shorter lifespan than normal blood cells. Signs of anaemia include: irritability, lethargy, tiredness, shortage of breath, pallor and, eventually, mental symptoms such as forgetfulness and confusion.

It is extremely important to establish whether the anaemia is due to a deficiency of B_{12} or folic acid because, although large doses of folic acid may make the blood revert to normal, this can obscure the more devastating degeneration of nerve endings that is characteristic of B_{12} deficiency.

Birth defects, such as spina bifida, and some complications of pregnancy, such as toxaemia, premature birth and haemorrhage following birth, have been associated with folic acid deficiency.

THOSE MOST AT RISK OF DEFICIENCY
Many experts believe that almost all of the population is on the borderline of folic acid deficiency.

Folic acid is required, in particular, during periods of rapid growth such as early infancy, and by pregnant women during the last three months of pregnancy.

Therapeutic uses

- Spina bifida. Routine supplements of folic acid have dramatically reduced the number of babies born with neural-tube defects such as spina bifida. This is a condition where the spinal column of the developing foetus fails to form properly, causing damage to the nervous system and resulting in severe deformities at birth, or early death.

- Schizophrenia. Folic acid, together with vitamin B_6 in some cases, has been used to alleviate the symptoms of schizophrenia.

LOSSES FROM FOOD
Cooking and processing vegetables, fruit and dairy produce can cause 45 per cent losses of the total folic acid. Cooking meat destroys between 30 and 50 per cent of the vitamin.

Loss of folic acid is accelerated by oxygen at high temperatures. In the presence of vitamin C, however, it is much more stable. The vitamin C in green vegetables should offer protection against loss of folic acid during cooking. But, because vitamin C is so sensitive itself, this may not happen.

Folic acid is sensitive to light, especially in the presence of riboflavin (vitamin B_2). It is also leached out into cooking water, so it is important to retain this for use. Vegetables are best cooked quickly in a minimal amount of water, with pan lids tightly on.

Sources of folic acid

Food	Microgram per 100 g total folic acid	Food	Microgram per 100 g total folic acid
Dried yeast	4,000	Almonds	96
Marmite (yeast extract)	1,010	Beetroot	90
Chicken liver	590	Cabbage	90
Blackeye beans	439	Chinese leaves	85
Wheatgerm	331	Frozen peas	78
Endive	330	Rye flour	78
Ox liver	330	Ox kidney	77
Brewer's yeast	320	Hazelnuts	72
Wheat bran	260	Parsnips	67
Calf's liver	240	Avocados	66
Lamb's liver	220	Walnuts	66
Chickpeas	180	Camembert cheese	60
Mung beans	140	Oatmeal	60
Tomato purée	140	Runner beans	60
Broccoli tops	130	Wholemeal flour	57
Red kidney beans	130	Peanut butter	53
Spinach	123	Chicory	52
Brussels sprouts	110	Egg yolk	52
Butter beans	110	Sweet potato	52
Peanuts	110	Sweetcorn on the cob	52
Pig's liver	110	Danish blue cheese	50
Spring greens	110	Pot barley	50
Turnip tops	110	Brown rice	49
Okra	100	Wheat	49 **
Red pigeon peas	100	Courgettes	48
Soya beans	100	Pig's kidney	42

Food	Microgram per 100 g total folic acid	Food	Microgram per 100 g total folic acid
Rye	42**	Dried peas	33
Ackee, canned	41	Oats	33
Spring onions, bulb only	40	Split peas	33
Cauliflower	39	Lamb's kidney	31
Wholemeal bread	39	Canteloupe	30
Oranges	37	Honeydew melon	30
Lentils	35	Egg noodles	29
Lettuce	34	Tomatoes	28
Spaghetti	34	Salmon	26

· spinach and mushroom salad ·

serves 4

This salad does great justice to the distinctive flavours of raw spinach and mushrooms.

4 tablespoons vinaigrette (see p. 239)
8 oz (225 g) button mushrooms
8 oz (225 g) young spinach leaves
2 spring onions
3 oz (84 g) sunflower seeds

Make the dressing before you prepare the salad vegetables, to avoid vitamin loss.

Wipe the mushrooms with damp kitchen paper, slice them thinly and place in a large salad bowl. Add the vinaigrette and mix in thoroughly. Cover and leave to marinate in the fridge for 30 minutes, stirring twice. Just before serving, wash the spinach and dry thoroughly in a salad-spinner or with kitchen paper. Remove any coarse stalks and tear into 1 in (2.5 cm) pieces. Put in the bowl with the mushrooms. Finely chop the spring onions and add to the bowl with the sunflower seeds. Toss all the ingredients thoroughly in the dressing and serve immediately.

· stir-fry broccoli with ginger ·
serves 4
Stir-fried vegetables make a perfect accompaniment for main courses.

---

2 tablespoons sesame seeds, toasted
1 lb (450 g) broccoli
1 in (2.5 cm) piece of root ginger
1 tablespoon unrefined, cold-pressed sunflower oil
$\frac{1}{2}$ teaspoon tamari (soy sauce)
1 teaspoon unrefined, cold-pressed sesame oil

Preheat the oven to 190°C (375°F, Mark 5). Spread the sesame seeds on a baking sheet and toast for 20 minutes in the middle of the oven, shaking them around once or twice, to prevent burning.

Break the broccoli into small florets. Retain the stalks and remove the tiny stems from the side. Cut the stalks diagonally into thin strips. Fill a large saucepan with water, bring to the boil and plunge the broccoli in for 30 seconds. Drain and retain the water for vegetable stock. Then plunge the broccoli immediately into cold water. Drain.

Peel the ginger and shred into fine strips. The easiest way to do this is with a lemon zester. If you do not have one, use the wide side of a grater. Heat the oil in a wok or frying pan on medium heat. When it is hot, stir-fry the ginger for a few seconds. (It should sizzle.) Add the broccoli and stir-fry for 3–4 minutes until heated through. Mix in the tamari and sesame oil and stir-fry for another 30 seconds. Transfer to a warmed serving dish and sprinkle with sesame seeds. Serve immediately.

· chicory, orange and hazelnut salad ·

serves 4

Chicory is a great salad vegetable because of its texture and beautifully shaped, pale yellow leaves. It can be slightly bitter but this is masked here by the sweetness of the oranges, and the creaminess of the dressing. This is an attractive salad for summer or winter. It goes well with rich main courses such as aubergine and cheese bake (see p. 187).

---

6 fl oz (180 ml) blue cheese dressing (see p. 245)
2 medium heads of chicory
2 oz (56 g) shelled hazelnuts, chopped
3 medium-sized oranges

Garnish
sprigs of fresh parsley

Make the dressing before you prepare the chicory and oranges to avoid loss of vitamins.

Remove the base stem from the chicory then cut the heads crosswise into thin strips. (It should fall away into strips or you can press them out.) Put in a bowl and mix with the blue cheese dressing. Place the chicory mix in the middle of a flat serving dish. Put the chopped hazelnuts in the middle of the chicory. Break the oranges into segments over the serving plate to catch the juice. If you remove the pith, chop up finely and sprinkle over the nuts.

Arrange the orange segments around the chicory, on the edge of the plate. Garnish with sprigs of parsley and serve immediately.

· spicy okra with yoghurt ·

serves 4

Okra or ladies' fingers are a popular vegetable in Indian cuisine. You can find them in some supermarkets, and Asian or Greek grocers. Make sure you do not overcook them, otherwise they will become soggy. Serve this dish with meat or vegetable curries.

---

12 oz (336 g) okra or ladies' fingers
1 green chilli
2 cloves garlic
1 in (2.5 cm) piece of fresh root ginger
2 tablespoons unrefined, cold-pressed sunflower oil
1 teaspoon ground turmeric
1 teaspoon ground coriander
1 teaspoon ground cumin
pinch of cayenne pepper
1 teaspoon freshly squeezed lemon juice
2 tablespoons creamed coconut
5 oz (140 g) natural low-fat yoghurt
sea salt

Garnish
Freshly chopped coriander leaves

Top and tail the okra and halve them lengthways. There is no need to remove the seeds because they are not hot. Top and tail the chilli, slit it down the side, remove the seeds and finely slice it. Crush the garlic and peel and grate the ginger. Heat the oil in a frying pan and add the garlic, ginger and chilli. Cover and cook for a few minutes. Stir in the turmeric, coriander, cumin and cayenne pepper and cook for a minute, stirring.

Add the okra and lemon juice, mix in well, cover and cook gently for 5–7 minutes until just tender. Grate the coconut and stir well in until melted. Remove from the heat and stir in the yoghurt. Season with salt. Garnish with freshly chopped coriander leaves and serve immediately.

· *blackeye bean and avocado salad* ·

serves 4

This is a substantial, colourful salad for summer or winter. The cooking time for blackeye beans is extremely variable. Do

183

not allow them to become too soft. Try herb dressing (see p. 240) for variety.

---

6 oz (168 g) blackeye beans
2–3 tablespoons tangy dressing (see p. 241)
2 large avocados, not overripe
6 oz (168 g) tomatoes
1 medium red pepper
2 spring onions

Soak the beans overnight. Drain. Cover with boiling water, return to the boil, cover and fast-boil, uncovered, for at least 10 minutes. Reduce the heat, cover and simmer for a further 35–40 minutes until just tender. (If using a pressure cooker, cover with fresh water, bring to the boil and simmer for 15–20 minutes.) Drain. Put the beans in a salad bowl.

Make the dressing now to avoid loss of vitamins from the vegetables through exposure to oxygen.

Remove the stones from the avocados, scoop out the flesh and chop into ¾ in (2 cm) cubes. Thinly slice the tomatoes. Cut the top off the pepper and remove the seeds, but not the core. Slice into thin strips, then cut into 1 in (2.5 cm) lengths. Finely slice the spring onions including the green part, and add to the beans. Toss the salad in tangy dressing until it is completely coated. Serve immediately.

· beetroot and red cabbage salad ·

serves 4

The distinctive feature of this salad is its bright red colour. Beetroot is usually sold cooked. Ask your greengrocer to save you some before he cooks it. For added texture, mix in some nuts, seeds or beanshoots. Try yoghurt dressing for a different flavour (see p. 244).

---

3 tablespoons vinaigrette (see p. 239)
6 oz (168 g) raw beetroot (about 3 medium-sized beetroot)

---

6 oz (168 g) red cabbage
2 medium oranges

Make the dressing before you prepare the vegetables to avoid loss of vitamins.

Remove the stalks and leaves from the beetroot and cut off the hard base stem. Peel and grate the beetroot into a bowl. Shred the red cabbage and add. Toss the salad in the vinaigrette until it is thoroughly coated. Arrange the beetroot and cabbage on a flat serving plate. Peel the oranges and break into segments over the plate to catch the juice. Remove the pith, cut it up very finely, arrange the orange segments round the cabbage and beetroot and sprinkle the pith over the top. Serve immediately.

· endive salad ·

serves 4–6

Curly endive is an attractive salad vegetable that makes a great change from limp lettuce. Endive is very popular in France, where you see different varieties on sale, including frisée and the more wavy Batavian endive. It is much more expensive in Britain and is harder to find. However, many supermarkets now sell it as a packaged salad with radicchio, its sister plant from Italy that looks a bit like a loose-leaved red cabbage. Like radicchio, endive can turn bitter, if it is not fresh, so make sure you eat it on the day you buy it or store in the fridge for no more than a couple of days.

---

4 tablespoons vinaigrette (see p. 239)
$\frac{1}{2}$ head of curly endive
1 small head of radicchio
10 Iceberg lettuce leaves
2 tablespoons pumpkin seeds

Make the dressing before you prepare the salad vegetables to avoid loss of vitamins.

Separate the endive into individual leaves, remove any very thick stems and break the leaves in half if they are very large. Separate the radicchio leaves and the lettuce leaves. Put all the leaves in a salad-spinner drum, rinse under cold water then spin-dry. Place the endive and radicchio leaves in a large salad bowl. Tear the lettuce leaves into about four strips and add to the bowl with the pumpkin seeds. Toss the salad in the dressing until it is thoroughly coated. Serve immediately.

· *courgette salad* ·

serves 4

The unusual combination of vegetable and fruit makes this an attractive, colourful salad. It is ideal as an accompaniment to dry dishes such as savoury millet, aduki bean slices or soya bean croquettes. If strawberries are not in season, try using oranges instead.

---

6 tablespoons (90 ml) honey and lime dressing (see p. 240)
1 lb (450 g) courgettes
3 sticks celery
1 green pepper
2 spring onions
8 oz (225 g) strawberries

Garnish
sprigs of fresh mint

Make the dressing before you prepare the salad, to avoid loss of vitamins.

Thinly slice the courgettes and celery and place in a large salad bowl. Remove the top from the green pepper and take out the core and seeds. Slice into thin strips, then into pieces $\frac{1}{2}$ in (1.3 cm) long. Finely chop the spring onions, including the green part. Remove the stalks from the strawberries and cut in half. Mix with the other ingredients in the bowl. Toss the salad in the dressing until it is thoroughly coated. Cover and refrigerate for 15 minutes. Mix in the dressing again before serving. Garnish with fresh mint and serve immediately.

· aubergine and cheese bake ·
serves 4–6

This bake is quite time-consuming but the effort is worth making, especially for a dinner party. Do not skimp on the olive oil because it gives the aubergines such a lovely flavour.

1½ lb (675 g) aubergines, preferably small
wholemeal flour for dusting
4–6 fl oz (120–180 ml) unrefined, cold-pressed olive oil
2 cloves garlic
2 medium onions
4 oz (112 g) button mushrooms
1 lb (450 g) tomatoes
½ teaspoon dried oregano or 1 teaspoon freshly chopped oregano
¼ teaspoon dried basil or ½ teaspoon freshly chopped basil
2 tablespoons tomato purée
sea salt
freshly ground black pepper

For the cheese topping

2 oz (56 g) unsalted butter or polyunsaturated margarine
2 tablespoons wholemeal flour
15 fl oz (450 ml) skimmed milk
¼ teaspoon ground nutmeg
pinch of cayenne pepper
freshly ground black pepper
5 oz (140 g) Cheddar cheese, grated
2 free-range eggs, beaten

Remove the stalks from the aubergines and cut into ¼ in (6 mm) slices. Dust them with flour on both sides. Heat 2–4 tablespoons of oil in a large frying pan. On high heat, quickly

187

fry the first batch of aubergines on both sides until golden brown. This should take several minutes and the aubergines should sizzle when you put them in the pan. Remove with a slotted spoon and drain on kitchen paper. Repeat the process, making sure the oil is hot each time, until all the aubergine slices are fried. (The amount of oil you use will vary according to how many batches of aubergines you have.) Preheat the oven to 190°C (375°F, Mark 5). Lightly grease a large ovenproof dish (at least 7 × 11 in (18 × 28 cm) and 1½ in (3.8 cm) deep).

Quickly prepare the other vegetables. Crush the garlic and finely chop the onion. Wipe the mushrooms with damp kitchen paper and slice finely. Skin the tomatoes by plunging them in boiling water. Leave for 1 minute, remove from the water and slide the skins off. Slice thickly. Heat 2 tablespoons of oil in the frying pan, put in the onions and garlic, cover and cook for 5 minutes. Add the tomatoes, mushrooms and herbs, cover and cook for a further 10 minutes, until the tomatoes become pulpy. Stir in the tomato purée and season with salt and pepper. While the tomatoes are cooking, make the cheese topping.

Melt the butter or margarine in a medium saucepan over a gentle heat. Off the heat, stir in the flour. Return to the heat and, stirring constantly, cook for 1 minute. Stir in the milk. Add the nutmeg and cayenne. Season with pepper. Turn up the heat, stirring constantly until the sauce boils and thickens. Simmer gently for 1 minute and stir in the cheese. Cook for another minute until the cheese melts. Remove from the heat and allow to cool slightly. Add the beaten eggs. You will now have a thin sauce that will thicken and set, to become the topping, once it is cooked.

Put half the aubergines in the ovenproof dish. Cover with half the tomato mixture. Put in the rest of the aubergines and cover with the other half of the tomato mixture. Pour the cheese topping over the tomatoes. Bake in the oven for 25–30 minutes until golden brown.

For extra folic acid
Serve with chicory, orange and hazelnut salad, endive salad or courgette salad (see pp. 182, 185, 186).

· *red bean stew* ·
serves 4

This wholesome bean stew is very simple to make. The fiery sauce will warm you up on a cold evening! To save time and to make sure all the toxins are removed, cook the beans in advance and store in the fridge.

---

6 oz (168 g) kidney beans
1 small onion
2 green chillies
2 cloves garlic
3 large courgettes
1 tablespoon unrefined, cold-pressed olive oil
2 14 oz (392 g) tins tomatoes
¼ teaspoon paprika
pinch of cayenne pepper
sea salt
freshly ground black pepper
2 tablespoons freshly chopped parsley

Soak the kidney beans overnight. Drain. Cover with boiling water, return to the boil and fast-boil, uncovered, for a minimum of 10 minutes. Reduce the heat, cover and simmer for a further 30–35 minutes, until just tender. Do not allow them to overcook, especially as they will be cooked further in the stew. (If using a pressure cooker, cover with fresh water, about double the volume of the beans, bring to the boil and simmer for 15 minutes.) Drain.

Finely chop the onion. Top and tail the chillies, slit the side and remove the seeds. (If you want the dish very hot, leave them in.) Chop finely. Crush the garlic and finely slice the courgettes. Heat the oil in a heavy-based pan, put in the onion, garlic and chillies, cover and cook gently for a few minutes. Add the courgettes, cover and cook gently for a further 5 minutes. Add the tinned tomatoes with their juice (breaking them up with the back of a spoon), beans, paprika and cayenne pepper, and season with salt and pepper. Cover, bring to the boil and simmer for 10 minutes to allow the flavours to permeate. Chop the parsley and mix in. Serve immediately.

For extra folic acid
Serve with brown rice or wholemeal pasta. Or, if you want a pleasant change, use pot barley. Serve also with steamed or stir-fried vegetables such as cauliflower, broccoli or Chinese leaf.

Biotin

Sources of biotin

Food	Microgram per 100 g	Food	Microgram per 100 g
Chicken liver	210.0	Oysters	10.0
Dried yeast	200.0	Pot barley	10.0
Egg yolk	60.0 a	Tomato purée	8.0
Wheat bran	45.0	Mackerel	7.0
Lamb's liver	41.0	Saithe (coley)	7.0
Calf's liver	39.0	Wholemeal flour	7.0
Lamb's kidney	37.0	Camembert cheese	6.0
Ox liver	33.0	Duck	6.0
Pig's liver	27.0	Rye flour	6.0
Eggs	25.0 a	Wheat	6.0 **
Wheatgerm	25.0	Wholemeal bread	6.0
Oatmeal	20.0	Cod	5.0
Oats	13.0 **	Haddock	5.0
Bloater, grilled	10.0	Halibut	5.0
Herring	10.0	Lemon sole	5.0
Kipper, baked	10.0	Lobster, boiled	5.0

Sources of biotin

Food	Microgram per 100 g	Food	Microgram per 100 g
Rye	5.0**	Blackcurrants	2.4
Salmon	5.0	Broad beans, boiled	2.1
Salmon, canned	5.0	Calf's brain	2.0
Sardines, canned in oil, fish only	5.0	Chicken	2.0
		Cow's milk	2.0
Globe artichokes, boiled	4.1	Goat's milk	2.0
Lamb's heart	4.0	Lamb	2.0
Plaice	4.0	Lamb's brain	2.0
Avocados	3.2	Turkey	2.0
Pork	3.0	Walnuts	2.0
Tuna, canned in oil	3.0	Raspberries	1.9
Redcurrants	2.6		

Note: **a** The natural antibiotic factor avidin, in raw egg whites, binds with the biotin in the yolk to form a complex unabsorbable by humans. Avidin in cooked egg white, however, is not active and therefore is absorbable.

· *chilled guacamole soup* ·
serves 4

This is a lovely light soup for a summer's evening and is very easy and quick to make – a good way to use up ripe avocados. If you want to make it for six people, simply add one more avocado and another 10 fl oz (300 ml) tomato juice.

---

2 large ripe avocados
2 cloves garlic
2 tablespoons chopped onion
freshly squeezed juice of 1 lemon
1 pt (600 ml) tomato juice
a few dashes hot sauce
pinch cayenne pepper
sea salt
freshly ground black pepper

Garnish
3 tablespoons freshly chopped chives or fresh coriander leaves

---

191

Halve the avocados and remove the stone. Scoop out the flesh and place in a blender. Crush the garlic, chop the onion and squeeze the lemon juice. Add to the avocados, with half the tomato juice. Blend on maximum speed until smooth. Add the rest of the tomato juice, the hot sauce and cayenne. Season with salt and pepper and blend until smooth. Transfer to a serving bowl or soup tureen, cover and chill. To serve, garnish with chopped chives or fresh coriander leaves.

For extra biotin
Serve with slices of wholemeal bread or pitta.

· *grilled herring with redcurrant sauce* ·
serves 4

Herrings are cheap, oily fish that can be quickly grilled or baked. You can also coat them with oatmeal and fry them in the traditional way. Look for firm, bright-eyed fish so that you know they are fresh. Ask the fishmonger to clean, bone and fillet them for you. Herrings need a good sharp sauce. Try gooseberries as an alternative to redcurrants or use frozen blackcurrants or go for a yoghurt sauce (see p. 250)

---

4 herrings, filleted (each portion of two fillets should
    weigh about 6 oz (168 g) in total)
unrefined, cold-pressed olive oil for brushing
freshly squeezed juice of half a lemon

For the sauce
8 oz (225 g) redcurrants
2 oz (56 g) raw muscovado sugar

Remove any remaining bones from the herrings with tweezers. Wash thoroughly, then pat dry with kitchen paper. Put the two fillets together. Slash the skin sides diagonally three times. Brush the slits with olive oil. Squeeze the lemon juice and sprinkle over the slits. Cover the grill pan with foil and place the fillets on top while you prepare the sauce.

String the redcurrants by running two fingers down the

192

stem. Remove any remaining stalk or stem. Put in a pan with the sugar on a gentle heat. Cover and stew for about 10 minutes until soft and juicy. Keep an eye on the fruit to make sure it does not burn. Transfer to a blender and liquidize to a smooth purée. To get rid of the pips, strain through a sieve back into the pan and heat through. Meanwhile, preheat the grill to high. Put the fish under a high grill and cook for 4–5 minutes on both sides until the skin goes crispy. Serve immediately with brown rice. Transfer the sauce to a jug and pour over the fish.

For extra biotin
Serve with brown rice or pot barley.

· *kedgeree* ·
serves 4

Kedgeree is a classic recipe for smoked fish, with an interesting blend of flavours. I have used kippers here to increase the amount of biotin. Buy undyed fish, if you can find it, otherwise try to buy it dyed with natural colouring. To save time cook the rice on another occasion and keep it in the fridge. Serve with a moist salad or steamed vegetables.

---

10 oz (280 g) long-grain brown rice
2 boned kipper fillets (about 8 oz (225 g) altogether)
1 small onion
2 green peppers
1 oz (28 g) unsalted butter or polyunsaturated margarine
1 teaspoon ground turmeric
2 teaspoons curry powder
4 oz (112 g) shelled unsalted peanuts
4 oz (112 g) raisins
5 oz (140 g) natural low-fat yoghurt
4 free-range eggs, hard-boiled
freshly ground black pepper

Garnish
sprigs of fresh parsley

Put the rice in a pan, cover with boiling water, return to the boil, cover and simmer for about 45 minutes until tender. Drain, rinse with cold water and drain again. While the rice is cooking, prepare the rest of the ingredients.

To remove the excess salt from the kippers, put them in a large jug, pour boiling water over them and leave for four minutes. Drain. Repeat the process. Skin the fish and flake into a small bowl. Finely chop the onion. Remove the top from the peppers and take out the seeds but not the core or pith. Slice into thin strips about 1 in (2.5 cm) long. Heat the butter or margarine in a large saucepan on a low heat. Add the onion, cover and cook until soft. Stir in the turmeric and curry powder and cook for a few seconds, then add the fish, rice, peanuts, green pepper, raisins and yoghurt and mix in well. Slice the eggs and gently mix in. Heat through thoroughly. Season with pepper and serve immediately, garnished with sprigs of parsley.

· fish pie ·
serves 4–6

White fish and mashed potato are pure comfort food for me. Perhaps it is because you do not have to make any effort to chew them! In this pie, the potato and the fish tend to go rather soft and mingle together. If you do not like this, slice the potatoes instead of mashing and fry them before you put them on top.

1½ lb (675 g) potatoes
2 teaspoons freshly squeezed lemon juice
1½ lb (675 g) firm white fish, for example cod, haddock
   or coley
3 large leeks
1 oz (28 g) unsalted butter or polyunsaturated margarine
2 tablespoons wholemeal flour
10 fl oz (300 ml) skimmed milk
1 14 oz (392 g) tin tomatoes

2 bay leaves
$\frac{1}{2}$ teaspoon paprika
$\frac{1}{2}$ teaspoon dried dill or 1 teaspoon freshly chopped dill
2 large free-range eggs, hard-boiled
2 tablespoons freshly chopped parsley
sea salt
freshly ground black pepper
2 oz (56 g) Cheddar cheese, grated

Peel the potatoes, keeping the peelings for stock. Put in a pan of lightly salted boiling water. Cover, return to the boil and simmer for 20 minutes or until just tender. Drain, retaining the liquid for stock. To avoid loss of vitamins, try to get the timing so the potatoes are not left for too long. Keep in a covered pan and do not mash them until the last minute. Preheat the oven to 200°C (400°F, Mark 6).

Sprinkle the lemon juice over the fish and steam in a sieve or a colander over a pan of boiling water for about 6 minutes until tender. Remove any skin or bones and flake the fish into a bowl. Finely slice the leeks. Heat the butter or margarine in a large saucepan, put in the leeks, cover and cook gently for a few minutes until soft. Mix in the flour and cook for 1 minute, stirring constantly. Gradually add the milk, stirring constantly, until the liquid thickens. Add the tomatoes (breaking them up with the back of a spoon), bay leaves, paprika, dill and fish. Slice the eggs, chop the parsley and gently mix in. Heat right through thoroughly. Season with salt and pepper, and transfer the mixture to a shallow ovenproof dish. Mash the potatoes and spread over the top. Press in with the back of a fork, making a ridged pattern. Sprinkle with grated cheese. Bake for 20 minutes until golden brown. Serve immediately.

For extra biotin
Serve with broad beans or treat yourself to globe artichokes.

· grilled plaice with tahini and orange dressing ·

serves 4

Plaice is a wonderful light fish that takes no time to cook. You can also use lemon sole. The rich, creamy dressing gives the fish a new dimension. If you prefer a sharper dressing, use lemons. You can buy tahini in most supermarkets, health shops and Greek or Asian grocers.

---

4 plaice fillets
unrefined, cold-pressed olive oil for coating
sea salt
freshly ground black pepper
tahini and orange dressing (see Variation, p. 247)

Garnish
4 tablespoons freshly chopped parsley
2 free-range eggs, hard-boiled and thinly sliced

Cover the grill pan with foil. Put the plaice fillets on the foil (you may have to do this in two lots), brush with a little olive oil and season with salt and pepper.

Pre-heat the grill to medium. While it is heating, make the dressing. Grill the plaice for 5–6 minutes (there is no need to turn it). Meanwhile, chop the parsley. Gently remove the fish from the grill pan and serve immediately with the sauce. Sprinkle the fish with chopped parsley and garnish with sliced hard-boiled eggs.

For extra biotin
Serve with brown rice or pot barley.

· blackcurrant mousse ·

serves 4–6

This light dessert is always popular with friends. If black-currants are out of season, use frozen ones. You may need to use more agar flakes to set the mousse, since they are not entirely predictable. You can find them in health shops.

---

8 oz (225 g) fresh blackcurrants or frozen, defrosted
2–3 tablespoons clear honey
2 teaspoons agar flakes
2 tablespoons boiling water
2 free-range eggs and 1 egg yolk
7 oz (196 g) natural low-fat yoghurt
flaked almonds to decorate

Top and tail the blackcurrants. Put in a pan with the honey, cover and cook very gently until soft. Keep an eye on them to make sure they do not burn. Add a little water if necessary. Allow to cool slightly, then put in a food processor with their liquid and blend until smooth.

Using the pan the blackcurrants were in, bring 2 table-spoons of water to the boil, stir in the agar flakes until dissolved, then mix the agar liquid with the blackcurrants. Whisk the eggs and egg yolk in a bowl for several minutes until plenty of air bubbles form. (If you don't have a separate whisk, you will have to return the blackcurrants to the pan, off the heat, while you use the processor.) Stir the eggs into the blackcurrants and mix in the yoghurt. Transfer to individual glass bowls or glasses. Cover and chill. To serve, decorate with flaked almonds.

17

·

VITAMIN C

·

Vitamin C is required in relatively large amounts. It is absorbed directly from the gastro-intestinal tract into the bloodstream and is then distributed throughout the body.

Vitamin C has a number of major functions. It is particularly concerned with the growth and repair of body cells and tissues, and is essential for making collagen, the fibrous protein that supports and protects the connective tissue of the skin, joints and vital organs of the body.

An important anti-oxidant, it has a mutually protective role with vitamin E and, together with vitamin A, beta-carotene, selenium and other protective substances, works to prevent the deleterious effect of free radicals (see pp. 92–3). Vitamin C detoxifies poisonous metals such as lead, cadmium, mercury and copper and other environmental pollutants like DDT. By detoxifying the body it also prevents cellular damage, which has important implications for protection against infections caused by viruses and bacteria, and against degenerative diseases.

Vitamin C is vital for the metabolism of various brain chemicals. It is involved in the production of natural cortico-steroid hormones which are produced by the adrenal glands and are required to combat stress; in the synthesis of nor-adrenalin, which has powerful effects on pulse rate and blood pressure; and also in the metabolism of cholesterol.

Its relationship with other vitamins and minerals

Vitamin C enhances the absorption of iron. This is particularly important since non-haem iron, found in foods of plant origin, is very difficult to absorb. It helps to convert folic acid into its absorbable form and protects it, to some extent, from deterioration in food.

Copper and aluminium accelerate vitamin C losses from food, so it is advisable to use stainless steel saucepans. Excessive vitamin C intake also reduces the absorption of copper.

Signs of deficiency

In its extreme form, vitamin C deficiency leads to scurvy. Signs of this include: bleeding, swollen gums, easy bruising and dry, scaly skin.

Early features of its deficiency include: depression, listlessness, muscle weakness and irritability. Other signs include easy bruising, bleeding gums and anaemia.

THOSE MOST AT RISK OF DEFICIENCY

Unfortunately, humans are unable to synthesize vitamin C. This means our bodies cannot always meet the extra needs for the vitamin, required especially during periods of stress, including injury and surgery, and infection.

Experts disagree as to how much vitamin C is required to keep the body tissues saturated. *It is advisable to consult a doctor before taking large dosages.*

Some people are more susceptible to deficiency than others. They include:

- The elderly. This is probably because the body reserves of vitamin C decrease with age. It may also be because of inefficient absorption mechanisms or simply because of poor dietary intake. Many elderly people, especially those who have lived in institutions for a long time, eat very few vitamin-C-rich fruits and vegetables.

- Smokers.
- Heavy drinkers.
- Pregnant and breast-feeding women.
- Women on the Pill.
- Those who have a poor dietary intake.
- Those regularly using certain drugs such as tetra-cyclin and barbiturates.
- Those regularly taking aspirin, which interferes with utilization of vitamin C.
- Those suffering from cancer.
- Those who have just had a major operation.
- Those living in a highly polluted environment.

Therapeutic uses

The common cold. Vitamin C has been used in the treatment and prevention of the common cold. Authorities disagree as to whether vitamin C actually prevents colds, but it does appear to relieve the symptoms in some individuals, provided it is taken in large enough doses, for the appropriate length of time.

Cancer. Patients suffering from a variety of cancers have been found to have a low body level of vitamin C and reduced immunocompetence. The vitamin may help to prevent different cancers, including:

- *cancer of the stomach*. This has been linked with increased intake of certain substances from the diet, notably nitrates – chemicals used for pest control – found in vegetables and drinking water, and nitrites – preservatives – found in cured meat, bacon, sausages and other such food. The latter react with amines in the stomach to form carcinogenic nitrosamines. Vitamin C protects the body against nitrosamine formation by detoxifying nitrites and, when they are formed, nitrosamines.

- *cancers linked to smoking*. By detoxifying cadmium, vitamin C may help to reduce the risk of cancers linked to smoking.

- *cancers caused by viruses*. Vitamin C has a well-established role in the protection against viruses. It may help to strengthen the body's immune system against these sorts of cancer.

- *growth of cancerous cells*. Increasing the amount of vitamin C in body tissues helps build collagen, which forms a protective barrier against the spread of cancerous growth through the cells.

Viruses. Vitamin C has been used in high doses with some success in the treatment of viral hepatitis, herpes, measles, mumps, poliomyelitis and other viruses.

Wounds. Vitamin C may help the healing of certain wounds because of its ability to make collagen.

LOSSES FROM FOOD
Vitamin C is the most unstable vitamin. It is sensitive to heat, light and oxygen and is destroyed by alkalis such as baking soda and some metals such as copper and aluminium. This means that it is easily destroyed in food processing and refining, and during storage, preparation and cooking.

To retain as much vitamin C as possible in fruit and vegetables, they are best eaten extremely fresh and raw.

STORAGE
Destruction of vitamin C starts as soon as fruit and vegetables are picked. Once they are exposed to the air, enzymes start to break down the vitamin, so the longer the period between harvesting and eating, the greater the loss of vitamin C. Freshly dug potatoes, for example, lose 15 per cent of their

vitamin C content after 1–3 months' storage and 75 per cent after eight months.

The worst losses occur in green, leafy vegetables because their thin leaves are not well protected and their large surface area is exposed to the air so the oxidation process is accelerated. Kale, for example, loses 1.5 per cent of its vitamin C per hour, once picked, so that one third disappears after the first day.

Storing vegetables in a cool place will help to reduce losses of vitamin C, but storage at freezing point or below causes damage within the cells of the leaves. This speeds up the breakdown of the vitamin.

The oxidation process is accelerated further by the handling and bruising of fruit and vegetables, so by the time they reach the shops, never mind your plate, considerable losses of vitamin C have taken place.

Fruit juices. These retain most of their vitamin C if stored in cans or bottles. However, once they are opened and exposed to the air, they lose vitamin C very quickly. Orange drinks, for example, can lose 30–50 per cent of their vitamin C within eight days of opening and 90 per cent after three weeks. The process of oxidation is made even worse if the juice is shaken. Apple juice loses 50 per cent of its vitamin C after opening and 95 per cent after 16 days. Juice stored in aluminium-lined cartons is likely to lose some of its vitamin C in storage.

Milk. Milk in glass bottles loses vitamin C rapidly because loss of riboflavin caused by light leaves a product called lumiflavin, that destroys vitamin C.

PREPARATION OF FOODS

Shredding, chopping and slicing. Losses of vitamin C occur very quickly because a greater surface area of vegetable or fruit is exposed to the air, to light, or to water if boiled.

Peeling. In some fruit and vegetables much of the vitamin C content lies in the skin. Peeling a Granny Smith apple, for example, causes 75 per cent loss of vitamin C. Machinepeeling causes greater losses than hand-peeling because the damage to the fruit or vegetable is greater.

Soaking. Soaking potatoes and root vegetables overnight causes vitamin C to be leached out into the water. Up to 60 per cent of vitamin C can be lost by soaking peeled potatoes in this way.

Blanching. Up to 60 per cent of vitamin C can be lost through domestic blanching, mostly because the vitamin is leached out into cooking water. To retain vitamin C after blanching, cool the vegetables very rapidly in cold water and retain this for use.

COOKING

Green vegetables lose on average between 50 and 70 per cent of vitamin C during cooking because it is lost into the cooking water and is also destroyed by heat. Leaving the vegetables hot for any length of time adds to the losses.

Potatoes lose much of their vitamin C through cooking and if they are mashed and kept hot, losses are increased. Average losses are:

	per cent		per cent
Boiled after peeling	20–50	Roasting	15–50
Boiled in their skins	20–40	Chipped or fried	15–30
Baked in their skins	10–40		

Sources of ascorbic acid (vitamin C)
The vitamin C content of the same foods varies considerably depending largely on the climate, season and soil; when the food was picked (if appropriate); and how it was stored, prepared and cooked.

Sprouted seeds contain large amounts of vitamin C. Research in the USA has found that they can contain as much as 600 times more vitamin C than the original seed. Once germinated, sprouts of 1 in (2.5 cm) can produce between 9 and 15 mg of vitamin C per 100 g.

Food	Mg per 100 g	Food	Mg per 100 g
Guavas	242	Lychees	40
Green chillies	235*	Mustard and cress	40
Red pepper	204*	Redcurrants	40
Blackcurrants	200	Turnip tops	40
Guavas, canned	180	White cabbage	40 a
Parsley	150	Loganberries	35
Kale	125*	Fennel	31*
Sorrel	119*	Ackee, canned	30
Broccoli tops	110	Mangoes	30
Green pepper	100	Mung beans, sprouted	30
Tomato purée	100	New potatoes	30
Red chillies	96	Spring greens, boiled	30
Brussels sprouts	90	Tangerines	30
Lemons	80	Melon	25
Kohlrabi	66*	Okra	25
Cauliflower	60	Peas	25
Savoy cabbage	60	Pineapple	25
Strawberries	60	Radishes	25
Watercress	60	Raspberries	25
Chives	56*	Spring onions	25
Red cabbage	55	Swede	25
Winter cabbage	55	Sweet potatoes	25
Spinach	51	Turnips	25
Oranges	50	Lentils, sprouted	24*
Limes	46	Chicken liver	23
White radishes	42	Chinese leaves	23
Gooseberries	40	Ox liver	23
Grapefruit	40	Apples, peeled	20

Food	Mg per 100 g	Food	Mg per 100 g
Blackberries	20	Potatoes	16 b
Flageolet beans	20**	Avocado	15
Passion fruit	20	Cooking apples, Bramley's, peeled	15 c
Tomatoes	20		
Leeks	18	Lettuce	15
Alfalfa seeds, sprouted	16*	Soya beans, sprouted	12*

Notes:

a 20 per cent is lost on shredding.

b Freshly dug main-crop potatoes contain 30 mg. The following reductions occur if stored:

Months	Mg
1–3	20
4–5	15
6–7	10
8–9	8

c Unpeeled Bramley's contain 20 mg.

· cauliflower and watercress salad ·

serves 4

A salad you can really get your teeth into. If you cannot get hold of chives, use spring onions instead. For variety use yoghurt dressing (see p. 244).

---

2 tablespoons tangy dressing (see p. 241)
8 oz (225 g) cauliflower florets (1 medium cauliflower)
1 bunch watercress
2 tablespoons fresh chives
2 oz (56 g) sunflower seeds

Make the dressing first to minimize loss of vitamins.

Break the cauliflower into tiny florets and put in a salad bowl. Add the dressing and mix in well. Rinse the watercress and spin-dry in a salad-spinner or pat dry with kitchen paper.

HEALTHY EATING

Remove any rough stalks if necessary and add to the cauliflower. Snip the chives into tiny lengths and mix in. Add the
sunflower seeds. Toss the salad in the dressing until it is
thoroughly coated. Serve immediately.

· red pepper and beansprout salad ·
serves 4

A distinctive salad that goes well with most dishes. You will
need to grow the lentil sprouts yourself, since they are not yet
available in supermarkets.

---

4 tablespoons sweet and sour dressing (see p. 242)
4 oz (112 g) beansprouts (sprouted mung beans)
1 oz (28 g) lentil sprouts
2 oz (56 g) alfalfa sprouts
2 large red peppers

Mix the dressing first, then place the beansprouts in a large
salad bowl. Separate the lentil sprouts and the alfalfa sprouts
into single strands, and add to the beansprouts. Remove the
tops of the peppers and take out the seeds and core. Do not
remove the pith. Cut the peppers horizontally into thin strips,
about $\frac{1}{4}$ in (6 mm) wide. Then cut them into 1 in (2.5 cm)
lengths. Mix in with the sprouts. Quickly toss the salad in the
dressing until it is thoroughly coated. Serve immediately.

· fennel, cabbage and apple salad ·
serves 4

Fennel is a delightful salad vegetable because of its unique
aniseed flavour, and texture. Its wispy top leaves can be used
for decoration. You will find it in most supermarkets.
Fennel seeds make an interesting addition to salads. You can
find them in some supermarkets, health shops and Asian and
Greek grocers. This is an impressive salad.

---

6 tablespoons peanut and fruit dressing (see p. 243)
1 large fennel bulb (about 12 oz (336 g))

---

2 medium, red dessert apples
4 oz (112 g) red or winter cabbage
1 teaspoon fennel seeds

Make the dressing first to minimize loss of vitamins.

Cut the stalks and the base off the fennel bulb and discard. Cut the bulb vertically in half and then into thin strips, about $\frac{1}{4}$ in (6 mm) wide. Put them in a salad bowl. Add the dressing and mix in well. Core the apples, cut in half vertically and then into thin strips, about the same width as the fennel. Shred the cabbage and add to the bowl with the fennel seeds. Toss the salad in the dressing until thoroughly coated. Serve immediately.

· kohlrabi, radish and turnip slaw ·
serves 4–6

Root vegetables have a certain sweetness that you can really appreciate when they are eaten raw. Unfortunately, grating tends to make them slightly watery. Kohlrabi looks like a cross between a cabbage and a large turnip and it has a slightly turnipy flavour. You can find it in most supermarkets. Celery seeds are available in some supermarkets and in Greek and Asian grocers.

---

3 tablespoons soured cream dressing (see p. 244)
1 medium kohlrabi
1 bunch red radishes
2 medium turnips
2 dessert apples
1 teaspoon celery seeds

Make the dressing first to minimize loss of vitamins.

Remove the stalks from the kohlrabi and cut off the hard base. Grate by hand or in a food processor and put in a large salad bowl. Mix in the dressing. Remove the leaves and stalks from the radishes and turnips. Slice the radishes thinly, and grate the turnips by hand or in a food processor. Remove the core from the apples and cut into thin slices. Add the celery seeds, turnips, radishes and apple to the kohlrabi. Toss the salad in the dressing until it is thoroughly coated. Serve immediately.

· russian red cabbage ·
serves 4–6

It seems criminal to cook red cabbage, especially for a vitamin C recipe but this classic dish is too good to omit. By the time I have cooked it, there is not usually much left for anyone else! It goes well with meat dishes, especially pork, and dry nut dishes or flans. To retain the wonderful crunchy texture of the cabbage, make sure you do not overcook it.

---

1 small onion
2 cloves garlic
2 tablespoons unrefined, cold-pressed olive oil
1 large red cabbage
2 tablespoons white wine vinegar
1 bay leaf
4 cloves
1 in (2.5 cm) piece of cinnamon stick
1 teaspoon allspice
1 large cooking apple
½ teaspoon raw dark muscovado sugar
10 fl oz (150 ml) vegetable stock

Finely chop the onion and crush the garlic. Heat the olive oil in a large frying pan, put in the onion and garlic, cover and cook for a few minutes. Meanwhile, cut the cabbage into quarters, wash and shred. Add the cabbage, turning it over so that it is all covered in oil. Add the vinegar, bay leaf, cloves, cinnamon stick and allspice. Cover and cook for 10 minutes. Wash the apple, core it and dice into ¾ in (2 cm) cubes. Mix in the apple, sugar and stock, cover, bring to the boil and cook for 25 minutes until the cabbage is soft but crunchy. Remove the bay leaf, cloves and cinnamon stick. Serve immediately.

· pineapple with raspberry sauce ·

serves 4

There is something really special about fresh pineapple that cannot be remotely emulated by the tinned equivalent. Unfortunately, it is so easy to bring home a pineapple, only to find that it is woody inside or 'off'. A pineapple should smell ripe but not too sweet. It should not be too soft to the touch, and the leaves should come away easily.

---

8 oz (225 g) fresh raspberries or frozen ones, defrosted
1 tablespoon clear honey
1 large pineapple or two small ones

Put the raspberries in a food processor with the honey and blend to a smooth purée. (Do not overwork, or they will not have any texture.)

Cut the top off the pineapple and put aside. Stand the pineapple upright in a small bowl. If necessary, slice a bit off the bottom to flatten it. Run a sharp knife round the inside edge of the pineapple, then scoop the flesh out with a spoon into a large bowl. Cut the flesh into $\frac{3}{4}$ in (2 cm) cubes, removing the core if it is too hard. Mix the pineapple pieces and any juice with the raspberry sauce and return to the pineapple shell. (There may be some raspberry sauce left over, which you can eat later.) Put the top back on the pineapple, place in the fridge and chill for 20 minutes. Serve immediately from the pineapple.

· summer pudding ·

serves 4–6

You need a good apron for this dessert because it tends to be messy! You also need time to prepare it and to leave it overnight. Use any summer fruit including mangoes, water melon, cherries or peaches – the more varied the mixture the better. You can use brandy, rum or kirsch instead of cassis. Any fruit juice concentrate, from a health shop, may be used as a sweetener. Grenadine syrup is a less healthy alternative. If you need more sugar, add it at the beginning.

8 oz (225 g) blackcurrants
3 tablespoons apple and strawberry juice concentrate
3 tablespoons cassis
2 tablespoons raw dark muscovado sugar (optional)
1 lb (450 g) mixed strawberries, raspberries, blackberries
  or redcurrants
7 thin slices wholemeal bread

Top and tail the blackcurrants, wash and put in a pan with the concentrated fruit juice and cassis, or alcohol of your choice. Bring to the boil, cover and simmer very gently for 5 minutes, stirring regularly. Hull the remaining fruit and mix in with the blackcurrants. Leave to marinate, covered, for 2 hours, mixing up occasionally.

Strain the juice from the fruit into a small bowl. Remove the crusts from the bread and cut one circular piece, large enough to cover the bottom of a 2 pt (1.5 litre) pudding basin. Immerse both sides of the bread in the fruit juice and cover the base. Cut 3 other slices to line the sides of the basin. Immerse both sides of the bread in the fruit juice and put in position. Gently place the soaked fruit in the middle of the lined basin. Press well down with the back of a spoon and level the surface. Cut the remaining pieces of bread down to size to cover the top of the fruit. Use to soak up the rest of the juice and put in position. If there is any juice remaining, pour it over the top of the bread. Place a saucer on top of the bread and press down. If possible, cover with non-PVC cling film. Place 2 tins on top of the saucer to weigh down the fruit. Refrigerate overnight. Gently turn out on to a plate and serve with single cream.

· *stuffed melon* ·
serves 4

Melons come in all different shapes and sizes depending upon in which country you live. Two popular kinds of cantaloupe melon on sale in Britain are Charentais and Ogen. The

Charentais has a deep orange flesh that is quite sweet and the Ogen is smooth-skinned with pale green flesh and a less distinct flavour. The Ogen is usually small enough to cut in half and serve as an individual starter or dessert, as it is used here. Galia melons have a raised, net-like skin which may be green, orange or yellow, with a crochet-type pattern. The flesh varies from green to peach colour and the flavour is light and delicate. Also known as musk melon, it too is small enough to cut in half for individual servings.

A good melon needs to be firm and plump and not bruised. When choosing a melon, press it at the opposite end to the stalk. If it is ripe, it should just give to the touch. If you shake it and it sounds watery, it is probably overripe.

---

1 tablespoon clear honey
freshly squeezed juice of half a lemon
2 small Galia or Ogen melons, well chilled
8 oz (225 g) strawberries or raspberries
2 kiwi fruit
fresh mint leaves to decorate

Mix together the honey and lemon juice in a large bowl.

Cut the melon in half, horizontally. Scoop out the seeds and discard. Gently remove the flesh with a melon scoop, leaving a thin rim round the edge and some flesh in the bottom. If you do not have a melon scoop, use a spoon and cut the flesh into $\frac{3}{4}$ in (2 cm) cubes. Put in the bowl and mix with the honey and lemon juice. Remove the stalks from the strawberries, slice thickly and add to the bowl, mixing in. Peel the kiwi fruit with a sharp knife, slice thinly, and add to the rest. Mix the fruit thoroughly with the honey and lemon. Spoon it into the four melon halves and pack in tightly. Decorate with fresh mint and serve immediately.

· gooseberry sorbet ·
serves 4–6
Gooseberries are a rare treat, because they are only in the

shops for a very short time. You can sometimes buy dessert gooseberries that are sweet enough to eat without sugar. However, if you can only buy cooking gooseberries, as below, you will probably need some form of sweetener. Do not be tempted to add too much, otherwise you will destroy the tart flavour of the fruit.

1½ lb (675 g) gooseberries
2–3 tablespoons clear honey
freshly squeezed juice of half a lemon
rind of 1 lemon
1 free-range egg white
fresh mint leaves to decorate

Top and tail the gooseberries. Put in a pan with the honey and lemon juice. Cover and stew over a gentle heat for about 10 minutes, until soft and pulpy. Do not be tempted to add more liquid as the gooseberries will become too runny, but keep an eye on them so they do not burn.

Cool slightly and put in a blender. Add the lemon rind and blend to a smooth purée. Transfer to a rigid freezerproof container, cover, seal and freeze for 2–3 hours until frozen but not rigid. Return to the blender and liquidize again, until well broken-up.

Whisk the egg white in a bowl until stiff peaks form. Fold into the fruit purée. (Keep the egg yolk covered in the fridge for use elsewhere.) Return to the freezer container and freeze again for 2–3 hours until firm. Ten minutes before serving, transfer to the fridge. Serve with an ice-cream scoop into individual bowls. Decorate with fresh mint leaves.

· fresh fruit salad ·
serves 6–8

One of the best things about summer is that you can eat so much fresh fruit. It is worth trying some of the more exotic fruit in a fruit salad, such as passion fruit, persimmons and papaya – in fact, the more colourful the fruit, the better. Fruit salad tastes best marinated for a short while in its own juices but this causes a loss of vitamins. If you do leave it to marinate, cover and put in the fridge.

---

5 fl oz (150 ml) white grape juice (optional)
1 tablespoon clear honey (optional)
1 lb (450 g) strawberries
2 oranges
4 oz (112 g) melon
4 oz (112 g) pineapple
1 small mango
2 dessert apples
2 kiwi fruit
2 bananas
4 oz (112 g) black, seedless grapes
fresh mint leaves to decorate

Mix together the grape juice and honey in a large bowl. Remove the stalks from the strawberries, halve or slice them and place in the bowl, mixing in with the grape juice. Peel the oranges with a sharp knife over the bowl to catch the juice. Break into segments. Remove any bits of pith and cut up into tiny pieces. Add the oranges and pith to the bowl and mix in well. Cut the melon, scoop out the seeds, remove the flesh and cut into large cubes. Mix in with the other fruit. Slice the pineapple, cut off the skin and remove the rough core. Cut into $\frac{3}{4}$ in (2 cm) cubes and, with as much juice as possible, add to the bowl. Peel the mango with a large knife so that you remove the skin and the bitter layer underneath. Scrape the flesh off over the bowl, catching the juice as you go. Core the apples, cut into thin slices and add. Peel the kiwi fruit with a sharp knife, peel the bananas, slice both thinly and add to the bowl. Remove the grapes from their stalks, add to the rest and toss the fruit salad in the grape juice and honey until all the fruit is thoroughly coated. Decorate with fresh mint leaves. Serve immediately.

18

·

VITAMIN D

·

Vitamin D is a fat-soluble vitamin that can be stored in the body. The body receives its vitamin D from two sources: from the diet, where it is absorbed from food into the small intestine and then into the lymphatic system; and by synthesis in the skin from the action of sunlight, after which it is released into the blood stream and transported to the liver.

Vitamin D works rather like a hormone and, with two other hormones, parathyroid hormone and calciton, regulates calcium and phosphorus metabolism. It promotes the absorption into the small intestine of calcium and phosphorus, both of which are necessary for bone formation. It also helps to release calcium from the bones into the blood, which then transports it round the body.

Signs of deficiency

Vitamin D deficiency leads to changes in the skeleton, resulting from a loss of calcium. In children, this causes rickets, characterized by softening and deformity of the bones. In adults, it causes osteomalacia, or softening of the bones with pain and stiffness in the joints, muscle weakness, loss of energy and many other bone-related problems.

THOSE MOST AT RISK OF DEFICIENCY

Because vitamin D can be stored in the body, it should be possible to obtain your required amount through exposure to sunlight in the summer, to supplement the diet during the winter. However, because of the vagaries of the British weather this is not necessarily the case; intake through diet has therefore become more important.

Some people are more susceptible to vitamin D deficiency. They include:

- The elderly.
- Those who are housebound.
- Dark-skinned people living in a northern climate.
- Those who live in a highly polluted environment where there is industrial smog.
- Vegans.
- Infants and young children, during periods of rapid growth.

Therapeutic uses

Rickets and osteomalacia are the only diseases known conclusively to benefit from vitamin D. It is possible, however, that together with calcium, adequate intake of the vitamin may contribute to the prevention of osteoporosis.

LOSSES FROM FOOD

Vitamin D is very stable in food and during cooking processes.

Sources of vitamin D

Food	Microgram per 100 g	Food	Microgram per 100 g
Cod liver oil	210.00	Ox liver	1.13
Bloater, grilled	25.00	Pig's liver	1.13
Kipper, baked	25.00	Butter	0.80
Herring	23.00	Lamb's liver	0.50
Mackerel	17.50	Double cream	0.38
Eel	14.00	Stilton cheese	0.31
Salmon, canned	12.50	Cream cheese	0.28
Pacific salmon	12.50	Parmesan cheese	0.28
Pilchards, canned in tomato sauce	8.00	Cheddar cheese	0.26
		Calf's liver	0.25
Margarine	7.90	Danish blue cheese	0.23
Sardines, canned in oil, fish only	7.50	Chicken liver	0.21
Tuna, canned in oil	5.80	Camembert cheese	0.18
Egg yolk	5.00	Edam cheese	0.18
Cod's roe	2.00	Single cream	0.17
Ghee	1.90	Goat's milk	0.06
Eggs	1.75		

Notes:

Vitamin D is also measured in international units (iu).

1 microgram of vitamin D activity = 40 iu

· *taramasalata* ·

serves 4

Taramasalata is a Mediterranean speciality, usually served with other starters, and pitta bread. Add all the ingredients very gradually, so they do not curdle.

---

4 oz (112 g) smoked cod's roe
3 large slices of wholemeal bread
2 lemons
2 cloves garlic
1 free-range egg yolk

4 fl oz (120 ml) unrefined, cold-pressed olive oil
pinch cayenne pepper
Garnish
sprigs of fresh parsley

Remove the skin from the cod's roe and discard. Soak the roe in cold water for a couple of hours to remove some of the salt.

Remove the crusts from the bread and soak it for several minutes in a little water or milk to soften. Squeeze the liquid out. Squeeze the lemon juice and crush the garlic. Put the egg yolk in a blender and blend with a little bit of oil on a low speed. Add the bread and the garlic and a little more oil and continue to blend slowly. Gradually add alternately the cod's roe, oil and lemon juice, until you have a creamy paste. If at any time the paste becomes unworkably thick, add a bit of water, milk or lemon juice. Finally, add the remaining lemon juice and cayenne pepper. Transfer to a serving bowl, cover and chill until ready. Serve with hot wholemeal pitta bread on individual small plates and garnish with fresh parsley.

· *segel's chopped herring* ·
serves 4

If you are Jewish, chopped herring is as familiar as baked beans on toast. If you are not, it is quite a delicacy. It is often served as a Jewish breakfast with hot bagels, cream cheese and smoked salmon.

If you live near a kosher fishmonger, it is quite simple to get hold of the right kind of herrings, otherwise ask your fishmonger for salted herring fillets. If he does not have them, you should be able to get them in a good delicatessen. Pickled herrings or rollmops are *not* the right sort of herrings.

You have to soak the fillets for 24 hours to get rid of the salt, so bear this in mind when you plan to make the dish.

---

4 medium-sized salted herring fillets
1 oz (28 g) wholemeal breadcrumbs

217

2 tablespoons white wine vinegar
1 tablespoon onion, chopped
1 large cooking apple
2 tablespoons unrefined, cold-pressed olive oil
$\frac{1}{4}$ teaspoon dark raw muscovado sugar
freshly squeezed juice of half a lemon
freshly ground black pepper

To serve
crisp lettuce leaves
1 free-range egg, hard-boiled and chopped very finely
thinly sliced toast

Soak the herring fillets for 24 hours, changing the water as often as possible. This is to get rid of the salt. Drain and wash under running water. Remove any bones and remaining skin. Chop finely and put in a medium-sized mixing bowl.

Make the breadcrumbs and put in a small bowl with the vinegar. Leave to soak for 10 minutes. Finely chop the onion. Core the apple and chop finely. Mix with the herrings. Add the soaked breadcrumbs, oil, sugar and lemon juice and mix thoroughly. Season with freshly ground black pepper. Serve with thinly sliced toast on individual crisp lettuce leaves and sprinkle with chopped hard-boiled egg.

· *pilchard spread* ·
serves 4–6

I have never forgiven my primary school for forcing me to eat pilchards because it left me unable to eat them for years. In fact, they are extremely tasty and the tinned products contain no colouring or additives. This is ideal for a lunch box spread, especially if you add lots of extras such as beansprouts, mustard and cress, tomatoes, alfalfa sprouts, etc. You can also serve it as a dip or pâté, garnished with fresh herbs like dill or parsley. Substitute sardines if you prefer, and if you do not eat dairy produce use soya cheese instead of cream cheese.

1 8 oz (225 g) tin pilchards in tomato sauce
4 oz (112 g) low-fat cream cheese or Quark (skimmed milk
  cheese)
1 teaspoon lemon rind
juice of 1 lemon
dash of chilli sauce
pinch of cayenne pepper
2 tablespoons freshly chopped chives or spring onions

Garnish
sprigs of fresh dill weed or parsley
lemon wedges

Put the pilchards, cream cheese, lemon rind, lemon juice, chilli sauce and cayenne pepper in a food processor and blend to a creamy paste. Chop the chives and mix in. Transfer to a small bowl, cover and chill until ready for use as a spread. Alternatively, spoon into a pâté dish, cover and chill until ready for use. To serve, garnish with sprigs of fresh dill weed or parsley and lemon wedges. Serve with hot wholemeal pitta bread or small slices of toast.

· *salmon soufflé* ·

serves 4

This soufflé is ideal for a starter or main course. I usually serve it with lots of new potatoes and a range of salads. You can do all the preparation in advance, except beating the egg whites which should be done at the last minute. Serve immediately, otherwise it will flop.

1 7½ oz (210 g) tin pink salmon
2 spring onions
freshly squeezed juice of half a lemon
1 oz (28 g) unsalted butter or polyunsaturated margarine
1 oz (28 g) plain wholemeal flour
5 fl oz (150 ml) skimmed milk

4 free-range eggs, separated
freshly ground black pepper

Preheat the oven to 190°C (375°F, Mark 5). Lightly grease a 6 in (15 cm) soufflé dish.

Drain the salmon, put in a small bowl, remove any bones and mash. Finely chop the spring onions, including the green part. Mix in. Add the onions and lemon juice to the salmon and mix in well.

Melt the butter or margarine in a medium saucepan over a gentle heat, sprinkle in the flour and cook for a few seconds, stirring. Add the milk slowly, and continue to stir over a moderate heat until the sauce is hot and has thickened. Remove from the heat and stir in the egg yolks, one at a time. Stir in the salmon and season with freshly ground black pepper.

Beat the egg whites until stiff peaks form. Gently and gradually fold them into the mixture. Spoon the mixture into the soufflé dish and bake in the middle of the oven for 30 minutes until golden and risen. Serve immediately.

· baked mackerel ·

serves 4

Mackerel is an oily fish that looks like a larger, more silvery herring. It is probably more popular in its smoked form, served cold with salad. This is a tasty way to eat it but does not do justice to the fish's delicate taste. When you buy mackerel, make sure the fish is fresh and bright-eyed. Ask your fishmonger to clean and fillet it for you. He will remove the head, tail and guts and rinse it. You may still find some bones, but these are easy to remove. Since mackerel is so rich, I usually buy one fish (that is, two fillets) for two people and the recipe below is for four people on that basis. If you find this too mean, you can buy more fish and double the quantities of stuffing. Serve with baked potatoes and green vegetables or salad.

220

2 large mackerel, filleted

For the stuffing
1 small onion
1 medium fennel bulb
1 large cooking apple
freshly squeezed juice of 1 lemon
1 teaspoon raw muscovado sugar
$\frac{1}{4}$ teaspoon ground allspice
1 oz (28 g) unsalted butter or polyunsaturated margarine
2 oz (56 g) wholemeal breadcrumbs
1 free-range egg, beaten
freshly ground black pepper

For baking
four cocktail sticks
unrefined, cold-pressed olive oil for brushing

For serving
15 oz (420 g) yoghurt sauce (see p. 250)

Garnish
sprigs of fresh dill weed
lemon wedges

Separate the mackerel into 4 fillets, if they are joined together. Rinse and pat dry with kitchen paper. Remove any remaining bones. Preheat the oven to 200°C (400°F, Mark 6) and lightly grease a medium-sized ovenproof dish.

To make the stuffing, finely chop the onion. Peel six leaves off the fennel bulb and chop finely. Core the apple, keeping the peelings for stock, chop finely and place in a small bowl. Immediately coat with lemon juice to prevent discoloration. Mix in the sugar and the allspice. Melt the butter or margarine in a frying pan, add the onion, cover and cook until transparent. Add the fennel, cover and cook for a few more minutes. Mix in the breadcrumbs and heat through. Mix in the apple, heat through and remove from the heat. Mix in the beaten egg and season with pepper.

Place the mackerel skin-side down and spread the stuffing evenly on each fillet. Roll up, skin-side out, making sure the stuffing does not squeeze out of the sides. Secure the rolled mackerel with a cocktail stick. Pack the mackerel tightly in an ovenproof dish. Brush the exposed skin lightly with olive oil. Bake in the middle of the oven for 30 minutes. While the fish is cooking, make the yoghurt sauce. Remove the fish from the oven, garnish with lemon wedges and a few sprigs of fresh dill weed. Serve immediately with yoghurt sauce.

19

VITAMIN E

Vitamin E refers to a group of substances called tocopherols, which are fat-soluble compounds that come in several different forms, all with different biological activities. Alpha tocopherol is the most potent; beta, gamma and delta, the other main tocopherols, are less active.

It works synergistically with selenium. In other words, they activate each other and are more powerful together than on their own. Together, they help the body resist infection caused by invading bacteria and viruses.

Vitamin E, selenium and vitamin C have a vital role as anti-oxidants. They protect the body against the harmful effects of free radicals which result directly or indirectly from radiation, atmospheric pollutants such as car exhaust fumes and tobacco smoke, and from some constituents of the diet. Free radicals are produced during normal metabolic processes, including the production of oxygen. When the production of oxygen becomes uncontrolled under their influence, the structure of cell membranes becomes damaged. This is the start of the degenerative process that causes disease.

Vitamin E helps to protect other essential nutrients such as vitamins A and C, polyunsaturated fatty acids and some amino acids from being broken down in the body and in the food we eat.

Essential for optimum muscle function, vitamin E helps to increase the power of muscles by ensuring they are fully supplied with oxygen and that it is used to maximum efficiency. Vitamin E also acts as an anti-blood-clotting agent. It dissolves blood clots, stimulating the formation of new channels for the blood and dilating the capillaries so fresh oxygen can reach them. It can help to prevent circulatory problems, including thrombosis, arteriosclerosis and heart attacks, and helps in the regeneration of new skin. It is excellent for healing scar tissue.

Signs of deficiency

Because of the slow turnover of vitamin E in the body, lack of it in the diet produces no clear-cut deficiency symptoms and signs in adults except, perhaps, generalized lack of vitality, manifested in lethargy, reduced sex drive and inability to concentrate. Vitamin E deficiency causes anaemia in adults and makes premature infants particularly prone to haemolytic anaemia. Irritability and oedema in these children may be associated with low levels of vitamin E.

Some conditions resulting from the inability to absorb fats may lead to vitamin E deficiency. These include: intestinal and pancreatic diseases, cystic fibrosis, cirrhosis of the liver and alcoholism. The characteristic feature of all these conditions is excess fat in the faeces.

THOSE MOST AT RISK OR DEFICIENCY

Little is known about individual needs for vitamin E. Requirements depend on intake of polyunsaturated fats and also vitamin A and amino acids. Ironically, vitamin E is often destroyed in the process of preventing polyunsaturated fats from oxidation. So, if your intake of polyunsaturated fats is great you will need more vitamin E to balance this. You may need more if you eat a lot of fried food and if you exercise frequently. If you live in a highly polluted area, your requirements are likely to be higher because of increased exposure to pollutants.

People who are most susceptible to deficiency include:

- Smokers.

- Premature infants.
- Alcoholics.
- Women on the Pill and those undergoing oestrogen replacement therapy.

Therapeutic uses

Premature babies. Vitamin E may help to reduce lung and eye damage that can occur in premature babies when they are given large doses of oxygen. It may also help to treat those premature babies suffering from haemolytic anaemia.

Blood circulation problems. Vitamin E has been used to help alleviate diseases of the blood circulation, including thrombosis, atherosclerosis, arteriosclerosis, varicose veins and phlebitis, where, for one reason or another, the flow of blood to organs and muscles has been restricted.

Cholesterol levels. Vitamin E has been used successfully to lower raised cholesterol levels.

Menstrual problems. Vitamin E has been used successfully to treat menstrual problems such as premenstrual tension, period pains and menopausal hot flushes.

Blood diseases. Certain blood diseases, such as sickle cell anaemia and thalassaemia, have in some cases responded to extra vitamin E.

Skin. Vitamin E, particularly in the form of ointment, can help repair wounds and damage to the skin from sunburn and scalding.

LOSSES FROM FOOD
Vitamin E is unstable and is partially destroyed by any refining and processing of foods. For example:

Producing white flour from wholemeal causes 90 per cent loss of vitamin E, because wheatgerm, which is its source, is removed. The bleaching process then destroys most of the rest.

Milling brown rice to produce white rice causes a 70 per cent loss of vitamin E. Parboiling the rice increases the loss to 83 per cent.

Flaking, shredding and puffing of cereals causes serious losses (for example, shredding wheat causes a 90 per cent loss of vitamin E and flaking corn causes a 95 per cent loss).

Solvent extraction of vegetable oils from seeds causes great losses of vitamin E. But cold-pressed oils, where the oil is squeezed out of the grain at high pressure, do not lose their vitamin E content. You can sometimes buy oils that have had vitamin E added, the advantage of these being that the vitamin E added is in a more stable form, which means that the oils do not go rancid so quickly.

Commercial storage also leads to considerable losses, for example, potato crisps lose 48 per cent of their vitamin E content after two weeks at room temperature. After two months, losses increase to 77 per cent.

Deep freezing causes substantial losses. One study showed that french fried potatoes, for example, stored at $-12°C$, lost 78 per cent of their vitamin E after two months.

Deep-fat frying increases losses of vitamin E from food. If frozen food that has been in the freezer for some months is fried in oil that has not had vitamin E added, then the food reaching the table will be practically depleted of vitamin E.

Sources of vitamin E

Food	Mg per 100 g expressed in alpha tocopherols	Food	Mg per 100 g expressed in alpha tocopherols
Wheatgerm oil	133.0	Asparagus, boiled	2.5
Sunflower seed oil	48.7	Butter, salted	2.0
Cottonseed oil	38.9	Spinach, boiled	2.0
Safflower seed oil	38.7	Parsley	1.8
Palm oil	25.6	Oatmeal	1.7
Polyunsaturated margarine	25.0	Eggs	1.6
Wheatgerm	22.0	Rye flour	1.6
Hazelnuts	21.0	Lobster, boiled	1.5
Almonds	20.0	Salmon, canned	1.5
Cod liver oil	20.0	Soya flour	1.5
Pecan nuts	19.8**	Wholemeal flour	1.4
Rapeseed oil	18.4	Broccoli tops	1.3
Peanut oil (groundnut oil)	13.0	Calf's brain	1.2
Corn (maize) oil	11.2	Double cream	1.2
Soya bean oil	10.1	Lamb's brain	1.2
Peanuts	8.1	Tomatoes	1.2
Cabbage, outer leaves	7.0	Sardines in oil, fish plus oil	1.1
Tomato purée	6.9	Spring greens, boiled	1.1
Brazil nuts	6.5	Blackcurrants	1.0
Tuna, canned in oil	6.3	Brussels sprouts	1.0
Crisps	6.1	Cream cheese	1.0
Olive oil	5.1	Parsnips	1.0
Peanut butter	4.7	Watercress	1.0
Egg yolk	4.6	Halibut	0.9
Rye	4.5**	Mussels	0.9
Wheat	4.3**	Oysters	0.9
Sweet potatoes	4.0	Parmesan cheese	0.9
Blackberries, wild	3.5a	Pot barley	0.9
Avocados	3.2	Soya beans	0.9**
Wheat bran	2.6	Brown rice	0.8**

Sources of vitamin E

Food	Mg per 100 g expressed in alpha tocopherols	Food	Mg per 100 g expressed in alpha tocopherols
Cheddar cheese	0.8	Greengages	0.7
Edam cheese	0.8	Mustard and cress	0.7
Green peppers	0.8	Pilchards, canned in tomato sauce	0.7
Leeks	0.8	Plums	0.7
Sweetcorn on the cob	0.8	Camembert cheese	0.6
Walnuts	0.8	French beans, boiled	0.6
Coconut	0.7	Carrots	0.5
Damsons	0.7	Single cream	0.5
Danish blue cheese	0.7		

Note:

a Cultivated blackberries contain 0.6 mg. Both contain other tocopherols.

Vitamin E activity is measured in tocopherols of which there are several forms. The most biologically active form is normally alpha tocopherol and the values stated above are for alpha tocopherol. Most oils, seeds from oils, nuts and some other plant products have other forms present. Their activity is as follows: beta tocopherol has an activity of around 30 per cent, delta tocopherol 15 per cent and alpha tocotrienol 30 per cent respectively of the alpha tocopherol activity.

· *cream of almond and spinach soup* ·
serves 4–6

This attractive, creamy soup can be eaten hot or cold. It is very popular with children. Serve with wholemeal bread or croutons.

1 small onion
2 sticks celery
8 oz (225 g) spinach
4 oz (112 g) shelled blanched almonds, chopped in half
2 tablespoons unrefined, cold-pressed sunflower oil
1 pt (600 ml) vegetable stock
10 fl oz (300 ml) skimmed milk
pinch grated nutmeg
sea salt

freshly ground black pepper

For the topping
2 oz (56 g) flaked almonds

Finely chop the onion. Scrub the celery and slice finely. Wash the spinach under running water and remove the stalks. Heat the oil in a large saucepan, put in the onion, celery and almonds, cover and cook for 5 minutes, stirring occasionally, until the almonds are golden brown. Add the stock, cover and bring to the boil, then add the spinach, making sure it is all covered with the liquid. Return to the boil, cover and simmer for 5 minutes until the spinach has wilted and is just tender. Gradually add the milk and heat through. Add the nutmeg and season with salt and pepper. Leave the soup to cool slightly then transfer to a blender and blend until smooth.

If serving hot, return to the pan and heat through. Transfer to a warm soup tureen and sprinkle with flaked almonds. Serve immediately. If serving cold, transfer to a serving bowl, cover and chill until ready for use. Sprinkle with flaked almonds to serve.

· *avocado dip* ·
serves 4

This is a very popular starter, with a soft, creamy texture. I often serve it with tortilla chips, just to set everyone's mouths on fire! Add more lemon juice and chilli sauce to taste.

---

3 medium-sized, ripe avocados
1 small onion
2 tablespoons mayonnaise
1 teaspoon wholegrain mustard
2 teaspoons freshly squeezed lemon juice
dash of chilli sauce
freshly ground black pepper
pinch of paprika

Stone the avocados and scoop out all the green flesh into a food processor or blender. Add the onion, mayonnaise, mustard and lemon juice and blend until smooth and creamy. Add the chilli sauce and season with pepper to taste. Spoon into a serving bowl, cover and chill until ready. Just before serving, stir the dip to blend in the colours. Sprinkle with paprika and serve on individual plates with wholemeal pitta bread or toast.

· sweet potato and apple soup ·

serves 4

This unusual soup is a delightful combination of fruit and vegetable. You can buy sweet potatoes in many supermarkets, and in Asian or Caribbean grocers.

---

1 medium onion

1 lb (450 g) sweet potato (1 medium sweet potato)

2 medium cooking apples

1 oz (28 g) polyunsaturated margarine or 2 tablespoons unrefined, cold-pressed sunflower oil

1¾ pt (1,050 ml) vegetable stock

½ teaspoon dried marjoram or 1 teaspoon freshly chopped marjoram

2 tablespoons freshly chopped parsley

sea salt

freshly ground black pepper

Garnish
fresh coriander leaves

Finely slice the onion. Peel the sweet potato and dice into ¼ in (2 cm) cubes.

Peel and core the apple, keeping the peelings for stock. Dice into ¼ in (2 cm) cubes. Heat the margarine or oil in a large pan. Put in the onion, sweet potato and apple, cover and cook for a few minutes, stirring occasionally. Add the stock, marjoram and parsley, cover, bring to the boil and simmer gently for 15–20 minutes or until the sweet potatoes are soft. Add more water if necessary, to prevent sticking. Put in a liquidizer and blend until smooth. Return to the pan, season with salt and pepper and heat through. Serve immediately, garnished with fresh coriander leaves.

· stuffed baked cabbage with cheese sauce ·

serves 4

The best cabbage to use for this dish is a loosely packed one like a Savoy. Other cabbages tend to be rather brittle, so the leaves tear easily. By cutting off the base, you can peel the leaves off easily without tearing them. Do not be tempted to put in too much filling, otherwise the parcels will fall apart.

---

4 oz (112 g) brown basmati rice

1 large green cabbage, preferably Savoy

1 medium onion

1 clove garlic

1 green pepper

1 oz (28 g) unsalted butter or polyunsaturated margarine

2 tablespoons freshly chopped parsley

2 oz (56 g) currants

1 free-range egg, beaten

sea salt

freshly ground black pepper

10 fl oz (300 ml) cheese sauce (see p. 251)

For the topping

2 oz (56 g) unsalted, shelled peanuts, chopped

Preheat the oven to 180°C (350°F, Mark 4). Lightly grease a medium-sized ovenproof dish. Place the rice in boiling, slightly salted water, cover, return to the boil and simmer for 5–10 minutes until soft. Drain.

Cut off the base of the cabbage and carefully remove 12 leaves. (Don't forget that the outside leaves contain the most vitamins, so these are the ones you should use.) Cut out the centre rib of each leaf with a sharp knife, then blanch each leaf in boiling water for 2 minutes. Drain, retaining the vegetable water for stock. Leave to cool for a short time, then remove each leaf carefully from the pan and gently pat dry with kitchen paper.

Finely chop the onion and crush the garlic. Remove the top of the green pepper, taking out the seeds and core, but do not remove the pith. Chop finely. Melt the butter or margarine in a large frying pan, add the onion and garlic, cover and cook gently for a few minutes. Add the green pepper, parsley, cooked rice and currants, mix in and heat through. Mix in the beaten egg and stir until cooked. Season with salt if necessary, and pepper.

Place the cabbage leaves on a clean surface, vein-side up. Put one heaped tablespoon of the rice mixture on each leaf near the base, fold in the sides and roll into a tight parcel. Pack the cabbage leaves tightly in the ovenproof dish and quickly make the cheese sauce. When the sauce has thickened, immediately pour it over the cabbage parcels. Sprinkle with chopped peanuts and bake in the oven for 30 minutes. Serve hot.

For extra vitamin E
Serve with sweet potatoes or parsnips.

· tuna rice bake ·

serves 4

This is a filling dish that needs only a simple salad to accompany it. Cook the rice on another occasion to save time.

---

8 oz (225 g) short-grain brown rice
4 oz (112 g) tomatoes
1 green pepper
1 small onion
1 tablespoon unrefined, cold-pressed sunflower oil

2 tablespoons freshly chopped parsley
2 7 oz (196 g) tins skipjack tuna
freshly squeezed juice of 1 lemon

For the topping
2 oz (56 g) unsalted butter or polyunsaturated margarine
3 tablespoons wholemeal flour
15 fl oz (450 ml) skimmed milk
4 oz (112 g) Cheddar cheese
1 teaspoon wholegrain mustard
$\frac{1}{2}$ teaspoon ground paprika
freshly ground black pepper
2 free-range eggs, lightly beaten

Put the rice in a pan of boiling water, return to the boil, cover and simmer for 15 minutes, or until the rice is soft, but crunchy. Drain and rinse. Preheat the oven to 190°C (375°F, Mark 5). Lightly grease an 11 × 7 in (28 × 18 cm) ovenproof dish.

Skin the tomatoes by plunging them in boiling water. Leave for 1–2 minutes. Remove from the water (keeping the water for stock), and slide off the skins. Chop into quarters. Remove the top from the pepper, and take out the seeds and core, but not the pith. Slice thinly, then cut into $\frac{1}{2}$ in (1.3 cm) strips. Finely chop the onion. Heat the oil in a medium-sized saucepan, put in the onion and green pepper, cover and cook until soft. Add the tomatoes, cover and cook for a few more minutes. Mix in the parsley and the rice, heat through and then press well into the base of the ovenproof dish. Drain the tuna fish and flake into a large bowl. Mix in the lemon juice. Spread evenly over the rice and press well down.

To make the topping, melt the butter or margarine over a gentle heat. Sprinkle in the flour and cook for 1 minute, stirring. Gradually add the milk, stirring constantly to remove any lumps. Raise the heat and bring to the boil, stirring, until the sauce thickens. Simmer gently for 1 minute then stir in the cheese until it all melts. Add the mustard and paprika and season with pepper. Remove from the heat and stir in the lightly-beaten egg. This will thin the sauce, but it will thicken when cooked to form a firm topping.

Pour the mixture over the top of the tuna and bake for 30–40 minutes in the middle of the oven until the topping is risen and golden. Cut into portions and serve immediately.

For extra vitamin E
Serve with stir-fried vegetables such as broccoli or leeks, or with a green salad.

· sweet potato cake ·
serves 6–8

Sweet potato is used a lot for puddings and cakes in Caribbean cooking. The dried fruit is normally left to marinate in rum or wine for a week or so, to make the pudding or cake moister and more tasty. I have added icing and a filling to make the cake richer, but it also tastes good without.

---

8 oz (225 g) wholemeal self-raising flour

1 teaspoon ground cinnamon

1 teaspoon allspice

4 oz (112 g) shelled almonds and hazelnuts, mixed and chopped

4 oz (112 g) mixed dried fruit

12 oz (336 g) sweet potato (1 small to medium sweet potato)

3 free-range eggs

3 tablespoons unrefined, cold-pressed sunflower oil

2 tablespoons clear honey

grated rind of half an orange

freshly squeezed juice of 1 orange

2–3 tablespoons dark rum (optional)

For the filling and icing
8 oz (225 g) low-fat cream cheese

freshly squeezed juice of half an orange

rind of half an orange

1 teaspoon raw light muscovado sugar

For the topping
2 oz (56 g) chopped hazelnuts

Preheat the oven to 190°C (375°F, Mark 5). Lightly grease an 8 in (20 cm) cake tin.

In a large bowl, mix together the flour, cinnamon, all-spice, chopped nuts and dried fruit. Remove the hard base of the sweet potato, peel and grate it, then mix in with the flour. In a separate bowl, beat together the eggs, oil, honey, orange rind, orange juice and rum.

Gradually add the wet ingredients to the dry and mix in thoroughly until all the egg mixture is absorbed by the flour. You will now have a fairly heavy cake mixture, but if you find it too heavy you can add a little milk. Spoon the mixture into the cake tin and spread evenly, right to the edges, levelling the surface. (As the cake is not of a runny consistency, this is particularly important.) Bake for 40–50 minutes in the middle of the oven until risen and golden. Leave to cool in the tin for a short while, then turn on to a wire rack. To make the icing and filling while the cake is cooking place the cream cheese in a small bowl, and beat in the orange juice, rind and sugar until you have a smooth, creamy spread. Once the cake has cooled, cut it in half. Spread half the cream cheese on the base. Put the top back in place and spread the rest of the cream cheese over it. Sprinkle with chopped hazelnuts.

· pecan pie ·
serves 4–6

Pecan pie is a traditional American dish for special occasions. It is very sweet! Pecan nuts are expensive, but they have a special delicate flavour. You can buy them in health shops.

---

9 oz (254 g) wholemeal shortcrust pastry (see p. 253)
8 oz (225 g) shelled pecan nuts
4 oz (112 g) unsalted butter or polyunsaturated margarine
8 oz (225 g) clear honey
3 free-range eggs
1 teaspoon natural vanilla essence

1 tablespoon brown rum
$\frac{1}{2}$ teaspoon ground nutmeg

Preheat the oven to 200°C (400°F, Mark 6). Roll the pastry out thinly and use to line a lightly greased 9 in (23 cm) fluted flan tin. Press in well and prick it all over. Bake 'blind' in the oven for 5–7 minutes, to set it. Remove the flan case and reduce the heat to 180°C (350°F, Mark 4).

Chop the nuts in half and sprinkle over the pastry base. Melt the butter in a pan over a gentle heat with the honey. Remove from the heat and beat in the eggs, one at a time. Add the vanilla essence, rum and nutmeg and beat in well. Pour the mixture over the nuts and bake for 40–45 minutes until the filling has set and is risen and golden. Serve hot.

For extra vitamin E
Serve with single cream.

· *hazelnut cookies* ·

makes about 10 large cookies

These biscuits are very quick and simple to make.

---

4 oz (112 g) shelled hazelnuts, chopped
3 oz (84 g) currants
1 oz (28 g) wheatgerm
3 oz (84 g) plain wholemeal flour
1 teaspoon baking powder
$\frac{1}{2}$ teaspoon ground cinnamon
4 oz (112 g) unsalted butter or polyunsaturated margarine
1–2 tablespoons clear honey
1 free-range egg, beaten

Preheat the oven to 180°C (350°F, Mark 4). Lightly grease two baking sheets.

Mix together all the dry ingredients in a large bowl. Melt the butter or margarine with the honey in a saucepan over a gentle heat. Pour over and stir into the dry ingredients, then mix in the beaten egg. You will now have a rather sticky mixture but it should be quite manageable.

Shape the mixture into 10 balls, about $1\frac{1}{2}$ in (3.8 cm) in diameter. Place on a large baking sheet with plenty of room in between to expand, and flatten with a palette knife. Bake in the middle of the oven for 15–20 minutes until golden. Leave to cool slightly then transfer to a wire rack. When cold, store in an airtight container.

20

•

ADDITIONAL
RECIPES

•

Salad dressings

Salad dressings are very important, not only to liven up the flavour of bland vegetables but also to coat them in oil, to prevent oxidation and consequent vitamin loss.

Vegetables and fruit start losing vitamins and minerals the minute they are picked. Once they are chopped, sliced and shredded, this loss is greatly accelerated because they are exposed to the air and light. Therefore, it is essential to: make the dressing before you start preparing the vegetables; prepare the salad at the last minute just before serving; and coat it in dressing and serve immediately. This will also mean that the vegetables do not have time to become soggy or discoloured. If, for some reason, you do end up leaving the salad, ensure that it is covered in non-PVC cling film to protect it from the air and put it in the fridge, to protect it from light and heat.

It is best to make and store salad dressings in an airtight container, such as a small jar. Most dressings will keep like this in the fridge for a few days and up to a week.

· vinaigrette ·

makes about 4 fl oz (120 ml) or 7–8 tablespoons

This is a very basic vinaigrette and is quite tangy. It goes well with all green salads, and with grain, pasta or bean salads. If you like it less sharp, you can add a touch of muscovado sugar. If you like garlic, crush in one or two cloves. You may also like to add 1 tablespoon of freshly chopped herbs like mint, parsley, chervil, tarragon, thyme or chives.

I always use wholegrain mustard, which you can buy in supermarkets. If you prefer ordinary French mustard, use that.

This dressing will keep in an airtight container for about a week.

---

6 tablespoons unrefined, cold-pressed olive oil
1 tablespoon white wine or cider vinegar
1 tablespoon freshly squeezed lemon juice
1 teaspoon wholegrain mustard
sea salt
freshly ground black pepper

Put all the ingredients in a screw-top jar and shake vigorously. Store in the fridge and shake thoroughly before use.

· honey and mint dressing ·

makes about 3 fl oz (90 ml) or 6 tablespoons

This is a lovely light dressing that goes well with summer salads like Chinese leaf and cashew (see p. 44). It tastes particularly good with mixed fruit and vegetable salads such as courgette salad (see p. 186) or Chinese leaf, watercress and peach (see p. 97). Fresh mint makes all the difference and if you do not have a garden to grow it in, you can sometimes find it in supermarkets. If not, you will have to use half the amount of dried mint. If you find the dressing too sweet, use less honey. You can keep this dressing in an airtight container for several days in the fridge.

239

2 tablespoons clear honey
3 tablespoons unrefined, cold-pressed olive oil
3 tablespoons cider vinegar
1 tablespoon freshly chopped mint
sea salt
freshly ground black pepper

Put all the ingredients in a screw-top jar and shake thoroughly. Refrigerate and shake again before use.

Variation

· *honey and lime dressing* ·
makes about 3 fl oz (90 ml) or 6 tablespoons

1 teaspoon clear honey
4 tablespoons unrefined, cold-pressed sunflower oil
2 tablespoons cider vinegar
freshly squeezed juice of 1 lime
1 teaspoon dried mint or oregano or 1 tablespoon freshly chopped
   mint or oregano

Put all the ingredients in a screw-top jar and shake thoroughly. Store in the fridge. Shake thoroughly before use.

· *herb dressing* ·
makes about 5 fl oz (150 ml) or 10 tablespoons

This is a delicious, light dressing that makes a potentially bland salad into something special. It goes well with bean salads, pasta salads or green salads. If you have fresh herbs growing in your garden or in pots inside, it will make all the difference. If you can't use fresh herbs, use half the amount of dried herbs. The dressing will keep for about a week, provided it is kept in the fridge in an airtight container.

6 tablespoons unrefined, cold-pressed olive oil
2 tablespoons white wine vinegar
$\frac{1}{2}$ teaspoon wholegrain mustard
1 clove garlic, crushed

2 tablespoons freshly chopped herbs (basil, mint, chives, parsley, thyme or tarragon)
sea salt
freshly ground black pepper

Put the oil, vinegar and mustard in a screw-top jar. Crush the garlic and mix in. Finely chop or snip the herbs and mix in. Season with salt and pepper. Shake all the ingredients thoroughly. Store in the refrigerator until ready for use. Shake again before use.

· tangy dressing ·

makes about 2 fl oz (60 ml) or 4 tablespoons

This hot, spicy dressing sets your mouth on fire! It tastes wonderful with vegetable salads such as cauliflower and watercress (see p. 205) or bean salads such as blackeye bean and avocado (see p. 183). It also goes well with bland, heavier salads such as buckwheat salad (see p. 110).

Fresh green chillies are on sale in some supermarkets and all Asian grocers. They come in all different sizes and are extremely hot. When handling chillies, do not touch your eyes or mouth and wash your hands immediately after preparing them, otherwise they can badly burn your skin. Keep out of reach of children. I have suggested you remove the seeds because many people find that they make the chillies too hot. If you want to make the dressing hotter, leave them in and add another chilli. You can buy dried red chillies from Asian grocers and many supermarkets. *Treat them with the same caution as fresh chillies.* You can remove the seeds in the same way. This dressing can be stored in the fridge for up to a week, provided it is in an airtight container.

---

3 tablespoons unrefined, cold-pressed olive oil
2 tablespoons freshly squeezed lemon juice
1–2 cloves garlic
1 medium-sized fresh green or 1 dried red chilli

241

1 teaspoon paprika
pinch of cayenne
2 teaspoons tamari (soy sauce)
freshly ground black pepper

Put the oil in a screw-top jar. Squeeze the lemon juice, crush the garlic and add them to the jar. Top and tail the chilli, slit it down the side and remove the seeds. (If you want the dressing very hot, leave the seeds in.) Slice finely and add to the jar. Add all the other ingredients and season with pepper. (Since the tamari is very salty, you don't need salt.) Shake all the ingredients thoroughly. Store in the fridge. Shake thoroughly before use.

· *sweet and sour dressing* ·

makes about 4½ fl oz (135 ml) or 9 tablespoons

This unusual dressing gives added piquancy to both leafy, fruity salads like Chinese leaf, watercress and peach (see p. 97) or wakame salad (see p. 26), and heavier bean, pasta or grain salads. Fennel seeds add a delicious tinge of aniseed to the dressing, but they're not absolutely essential. You can buy them from health shops or Asian grocers. The dressing needs to be mixed in well, otherwise all the juice sinks to the bottom of the bowl. You can keep the dressing in the fridge for about a week, provided it is in an airtight container.

---

4 tablespoons unrefined, cold-pressed sunflower oil
1 tablespoon cider vinegar
3 tablespoons unsweetened pineapple juice
1 tablespoon tamari (soy sauce)
½ teaspoon crushed whole fennel seeds
juice of half an orange
½ in (1.3 cm) piece of fresh root ginger
sea salt
freshly ground black pepper

Mix the oil, vinegar, pineapple juice and tamari together in a screw-top jar. Crush the fennel seeds with a pestle and mortar or in a grinder. Mix with the other ingredients. Squeeze the orange juice and mix in well. Peel the ginger and grate into the jar. Season with salt and pepper. Shake thoroughly until all the ingredients are mixed in well. Store in the fridge. Shake thoroughly before use.

· peanut and fruit dressing ·

makes about 6 fl oz (180 ml) or about 12 tablespoons

This naturally sweet dressing is perfect for salads with a strong texture such as fennel, cabbage and apple (see p. 206) or kohlrabi, radish and turnip slaw (see p. 207). It has a strong, fruity flavour, which also lends itself to moist salads made with a combination of fruit and vegetables. You need to toss the salad well, otherwise the dressing sinks to the bottom of the bowl. If you can get hold of limes, they're worth using because they give the dressing a sharp edge and, of course, they contain lots of vitamin C. Lemons will do just as well. Provided you keep the dressing in an airtight container in the fridge, it should last several days.

---

2 tablespoons smooth peanut butter, sugar-free
3 tablespoons unsweetened pineapple juice
juice of 1 orange
juice of half a lime or lemon
grated rind of half a lime or lemon

Put the peanut butter in a blender, add the pineapple juice and blend on low speed. (If you do not have a blender, gently beat together in a small bowl.) Squeeze the orange juice and lime juice and add to the peanut butter. Grate the lime rind and add. Blend all the ingredients until smooth and creamy. Transfer to a screw-top jar and store in the fridge until ready for use.

· soured cream dressing ·

makes about 5 fl oz (150 ml) or 10 tablespoons

This rich dressing is perfect for salads made with vegetables with a strong texture, such as beetroot and red cabbage (see p. 184) or chicory, orange and hazelnut (see p. 182). It is ideal for slaws and root vegetable-based salads such as kohlrabi, radish and turnip (see p. 207).

It is very rich, high in saturated fat and calories, so I only use it for special occasions. My own feeling is that low-fat yoghurt serves very much the same purpose as soured cream, with the advantage of containing less fat. Provided you keep all the ingredients in an airtight container in the fridge, this dressing should keep for one or two days.

---

5 fl oz (150 ml) soured cream
1 tablespoon cider vinegar
2 teaspoons freshly squeezed lemon juice
1 clove garlic, crushed
½ teaspoon wholegrain mustard
sea salt
freshly ground black pepper

Put all the ingredients in a small bowl and beat lightly until blended to a creamy mixture. Transfer to an air-tight container and refrigerate. Mix in again before use.

· yoghurt dressing ·

makes about 5 fl oz (150 ml) or 10 tablespoons

This delightful dressing goes well with heavier salads such as beetroot and red cabbage (see p. 184), most light vegetable salads such as cauliflower and watercress salad (see p. 205) and all sorts of slaws, as an alternative to mayonnaise.

This dressing is very basic – you can embellish it in all sorts of ways, depending upon which salad you are using it with. If you like it very rich and creamy, you can make it with Greek yoghurt. You can store it in the fridge for about a week, provided it is in an airtight container.

---

1 5 oz (140 g) carton natural low-fat yoghurt
juice of half a lemon
1 clove garlic
sea salt
freshly ground black pepper

Beat the yoghurt slightly to mix in the liquid. Transfer to a screw-top jar. Squeeze the lemon juice and mix in with a fork. Crush the garlic and mix in. Season with salt and pepper. Mix all the ingredients in thoroughly. Store in the fridge and mix in again before use.

Variations

- Add ½ to 1 teaspoon clear honey to make the dressing slightly sweet.

- Add 2 tablespoons freshly chopped mint, parsley, spring onion, chives or watercress.

- For a spicy effect, add ½ to 1 teaspoon ground whole spices, for example, coriander or cumin seeds, crushed in a pestle and mortar or in a grinder; 1 teaspoon curry powder; a pinch of cayenne pepper; or ¼ teaspoon chilli powder.

· *blue cheese dressing* ·
makes about 6 fl oz (180 ml) or 12 tablespoons

This is a rich, creamy dressing that I only use for special occasions because it is high in saturated fat and calories. I adore Danish blue cheese, but many people find it overpowering. It is perfect for livening up salad vegetables, especially those with some texture such as celery, cabbage or Chinese leaf, or root vegetables such as turnip. It is also good for tempering those with a slightly bitter taste such as chicory, endive or watercress and it goes well with nuts. It will keep, in an airtight container in the fridge, for a day.

---

3 oz (84 g) Danish blue cheese
5 oz (140 g) Greek yoghurt or low-fat natural-set yoghurt
juice of $\frac{1}{2}$ a lemon
1 clove garlic
1 tablespoon chopped chives
sea salt
freshly ground black pepper

Crumble the blue cheese into a food processor or blender. (If you do not have a blender beat all the ingredients together in a small bowl.) Add the yoghurt. Squeeze the lemon juice, crush the garlic and add to the other ingredients in the blender. Blend on low speed until you have a smooth creamy dressing. Chop the chives and mix in well. Season with salt and pepper. Transfer to an airtight container and store in the fridge. Mix in again before use.

· tahini and orange dressing ·

makes about 2 fl oz (60 ml) or 4 tablespoons

This is an unusual, nutty dressing that goes well with both root vegetable salads and green salads. Although tahini is quite dry, the orange juice in this dressing makes it moister and produces a smooth, creamy dressing. It takes some getting used to, and is fairly rich.

You will find tahini (sesame spread) in health shops and all Greek grocers. You can experiment with any of the nut or seed spreads available in health shops, for example, sunflower spread, hazelnut or almond. If you prefer a slightly sharper dressing, use lemon juice instead. I usually make this dressing in a jar rather than in the blender, because I feel I have more control over the outcome and there is less washing up! If you use a blender, mix the dressing on low speed. It will keep in an airtight container in the fridge for about a week.

2 tablespoons tahini (sesame spread)
1 tablespoon unrefined, cold-pressed olive oil
2 tablespoons water
freshly squeezed juice of 1 orange
$\frac{1}{2}$ in (1.3 cm) piece of fresh root ginger

Beat the tahini and olive oil together with a fork, in a screw-top jar. Beat in the water, trying to make sure the tahini does not curdle. Squeeze the orange juice and mix in well. Peel the ginger, grate finely and add to the other ingredients. Make sure all the ingredients are well mixed together. Refrigerate and beat together just before use.

Variation

● Use 9 oz (254 g) tahini, 2 cloves garlic and freshly squeezed juice of 2 oranges to make the dressing that goes with Grilled Plaice (see p. 196). Put the tahini in a blender, crush the garlic and mix in, then gradually blend in the orange juice until you have a thick, creamy paste. If too thick, gradually add some water and mix in well.

· *mayonnaise* ·

makes about 10 fl oz (300 ml) or 20 tablespoons

Mayonnaise is always worth making yourself if you have time, and you can keep it for about two days provided you store it in an airtight container in the fridge.

If you keep your eggs in the refrigerator get them out in advance, because if the yolks are too cold they may make the mayonnaise curdle. (You will have to cover up the egg whites, refrigerate and use in another recipe.)

You can make the mayonnaise either in a blender or, if you prefer, in a bowl. I prefer making it in a bowl, because I feel I have more control over the outcome. The main thing to remember in making mayonnaise is that the oil should be added very gradually, otherwise it may cause the mayonnaise to curdle.

---

2 free-range egg yolks
2 teaspoons wine or cider vinegar
$\frac{1}{4}$ teaspoon wholegrain mustard
$\frac{1}{4}$ teaspoon sea salt
10 fl 1 oz (300 ml) unrefined, cold-pressed olive oil
    or sunflower oil or a mixture of both

Using a balloon whisk beat the egg yolks in a bowl until light and creamy. Beat in the vinegar, mustard and salt. Add half the oil, drop by drop, beating all the time – the easiest way to do this is by pouring it gently down the back of a fork, beating it with the fork, as you go – until the mixture thickens. Keep adding the oil in small quantities, beating constantly, until it has all been used up and you have a thick mayonnaise.

If using a blender, put in the egg yolks, add the vinegar, mustard and salt and blend on a low speed for 10 seconds. Keep the blender on and feed in half the oil drop by drop until the mixture thickens. Add the rest of the oil, very slowly, in small quantities, with the blender on a low speed, until you have a thick mayonnaise. Transfer to an airtight container and store in the fridge until ready for use.

· *tropical dressing* ·

makes about 3 fl oz (90 ml) or 6 tablespoons

A light, slightly tangy dressing that goes well with rice dishes like Tropical Rice salad (see p. 44).

---

2 tablespoons unrefined, cold-pressed sunflower oil
1 tablespoon white wine vinegar
3 tablespoons unsweetened pineapple juice
$\frac{1}{2}$ teaspoon fresh root ginger, peeled and grated
sea salt
freshly ground black pepper

Put all the ingredients in a screw-top jar and shake thoroughly. Store in the refrigerator until ready for use. Shake again before using.

Sauces

Sauces are especially important for dry dishes made with pasta, rice or other grains; bean loaves and cutlets, hamburgers, fish, etc. I have provided a few very basic ones for you to try:

· *tomato sauce* ·
makes just over 2 pt (1,200 ml)

This is a fairly basic thick tomato sauce. I usually make large quantities and freeze it. Tomato sauce is extremely versatile; it goes well with many different dishes. For example, it is a very important part of many Italian dishes and tastes delicious on its own with pasta. It is ideal for dry fish cakes or bean burgers; added to a plain rice dish or with barley and other grains. You can do all sorts of things to make the sauce more interesting. You can add red wine with the tomatoes or a little sugar to make it a bit sweeter. When you are frying the onions, celery and garlic, you can add a bouquet garni and bay leaf. Just before serving you can add freshly chopped parsley and other herbs. If you want to make it hot, you can add paprika, chilli powder and cayenne pepper to taste.

---

2 large onions
4 sticks celery
4 cloves garlic
2 tablespoons olive oil
2 medium-sized carrots
2 14 oz (392 g) tins tomatoes
4 tablespoons tomato purée
½ teaspoon dried oregano or 1 teaspoon freshly
  chopped oregano

pinch of dried basil or ½ teaspoon freshly chopped basil
freshly ground black pepper
pinch of sea salt

Finely chop the onion, thinly slice the celery and crush the garlic. Heat the oil in a large frying pan or saucepan. Add the onion, garlic and celery, cover and cook for a few minutes. Scrub the carrots and dice into ¼ in (6 mm) cubes. Mix with the other ingredients in the pan, cover and cook for 5 minutes. Add the tomatoes with their juice (breaking them up with the back of a wooden spoon). Stir in the tomato purée. Bring to the boil, cover and simmer gently for 10–15 minutes, until you have a thick sauce. Stir occasionally. Add the oregano and basil and season with salt and pepper.

For a smooth sauce, transfer to a blender and liquidize. Return to the pan and heat through. If you want to thin down, simply add water.

· yoghurt sauce ·

Yoghurt sauce is a perfect accompaniment to hot dishes like spicy chickpeas or spinach and lentil curry (see pp. 45, 60). It is ideal to serve with fish such as herring or mackerel; tomato dishes, bean loaves and rissoles. The recipe below is very simple; you can embellish it in all sorts of ways. Yoghurt sauce will keep in an airtight container in the fridge for a week.

---

1 15 oz (420 g) carton natural low-fat yoghurt
freshly squeezed juice of 1 lemon
2 cloves garlic
2–3 tablespoons freshly chopped parsley
pinch of paprika
sea salt
freshly ground black pepper

Put the yoghurt into a small serving bowl and beat lightly to mix in the liquid. Squeeze the lemon juice, crush the garlic, chop the parsley and mix all three in. Add the paprika and season with salt and pepper. Cover and chill until ready for use.

Variation

- To make hotter, add a pinch of cayenne pepper or $\frac{1}{4}$ teaspoon chilli powder.

- To embellish, add different freshly chopped herbs such as chives, sorrel or fennel or add chopped spring onion or watercress.

· *cheese sauce* ·
makes 10 fl oz (300 ml)

This sauce can be used with so many different foods such as Broccoli and Almond Lasagne (see p. 28); Beef Lasagne (see p. 80); Chestnut Bake (see p. 126); Stuffed Baked Cabbage (see p. 231).

---

1 oz (28 g) unsalted butter
1 tablespoon wholemeal flour
10 fl oz (300 ml) skimmed milk
4 oz (112 g) Cheddar cheese, grated
1 teaspoon wholegrain mustard

Melt the butter or margarine in a medium saucepan, over a gentle heat. Remove from the heat and stir in the flour, then cook gently for 1–2 minutes, stirring constantly. Gradually stir in the milk, making sure there are no lumps. Bring to the boil and simmer for 3–4 minutes. While the sauce is simmering, stir in the grated cheese and the mustard. Season with pepper.

Variation

- Quantities vary for Beef Lasagne (see p. 80): $1\frac{1}{2}$ oz (42 g) unsalted butter, $1\frac{1}{2}$ oz (42 g) wholemeal flour, 1 pt (600 ml) skimmed milk, 6 oz (168 g) Cheddar cheese grated, pinch of nutmeg, sea salt, black pepper, but no mustard.

· sweet and sour sauce ·

makes 3½ fl oz (105 ml) or 7 tablespoons

A popular sauce that goes well with meat and vegetables.

---

2 teaspoons arrowroot
2 teaspoons water
1 tablespoon cider vinegar
1 tablespoon tamari (soy sauce)
4 tablespoons pineapple juice
1 tablespoon sugar
1 tablespoon tomato purée
1 teaspoon unrefined, cold-pressed sesame oil

To make the sweet and sour sauce, put the arrowroot in a small bowl and blend in the water to make a smooth paste. Add the vinegar, tamari, pineapple juice, sugar, tomato purée and sesame oil and mix well in.

· onion gravy ·

makes about 2 pt (1,200 ml)

This is a very basic 'vegetarian' gravy that can be used to moisten nut roasts or bean loaves. It also tastes good with meat, rice and other grain dishes. It freezes well, so it is a good idea to make a large amount and freeze it.

---

2 large onions
2 tablespoons (30 ml) unrefined, cold-pressed sunflower oil
2 tablespoons wholemeal flour
15 fl oz (450 ml) vegetable stock
1 teaspoon yeast extract
1 teaspoon (5 ml) tamari (soy sauce)
1 tablespoon tomato purée
1 bay leaf
¼ teaspoon dried thyme or 1 teaspoon freshly chopped thyme
freshly ground black pepper

Finely chop the onions. Heat the oil in a large frying pan, then add the onions, cover and cook gently until golden brown. Stir in the flour and cook for 2 minutes, stirring constantly.

Gradually add the vegetable stock, stirring all the time. Add the yeast extract, tamari and tomato purée and stir in well. Bring to the boil and add the bay leaf and thyme. Cover and simmer for about five minutes, stirring occasionally. Season with pepper to taste.

If you want a smooth gravy, transfer the mixture to a food processor or blender, and blend until smooth. Return to the pan and heat through. I prefer to retain the texture of the onions so I do not liquidize them.

Miscellaneous

· wholemeal shortcrust pastry ·

makes approximately 10 oz (280 g) of pastry.
Suitable for a 9 in (23 cm) flan case or quiche dish, with
a little left over.

You probably have your own pet way of making pastry because you know what works for you. My mother always taught me that the essence of good pastry was to keep it cold, handle it as little as possible and roll it out thinly.

You may find wholemeal pastry harder to handle at first because it is less elastic than pastry made with refined white flour. It is much denser and coarser and it does not always stick together. Many people use a mixture of wholemeal and white flour for this reason. However, like everything else, practice makes perfect.

Because the absorption qualities of wholemeal flour may vary a little, you may need to add more water, fat or oil to make the dough into a workable consistency. It is advisable to leave the dough for about 30 minutes before use, to give the fibre a chance to absorb the liquid and to swell. This obviously adds to the cooking time, but makes a much better pastry. If you are concerned about the possible carcinogenic properties of cling film, you can use non-PVC food wrap or simply put the pastry in an airtight container in the fridge. Pastry freezes quite well so you can make double quantities. I usually find that when it has been frozen, it is slightly less manageable and tends to break up. A little bit of oil added usually does the trick.

---

7 oz (196 g) 100 per cent wholemeal flour (plain)

2 teaspoons baking powder

$3\frac{1}{2}$ oz (98 g) fat (butter, solid vegetable margarine, polyunsaturated margarine or a mixture)

4–5 tablespoons (60–75 ml) cold water

Place the flour and baking powder in a mixing bowl. Mix the baking powder well in to distribute evenly. Cut the fat into small pieces and, using your fingertips, rub it into the flour until it resembles fine wholemeal breadcrumbs. Make a well in the middle. Pour in the water and fold in the flour with a round-edged knife until the mixture begins to stick together. Use your hands to bring the pieces together, and gently shape into a ball, making a soft, manageable dough. Add more water if necessary, to give a workable consistency, or add a little oil. Wrap the pastry in non-PVC cling film and leave in a cool place for 30 minutes. Turn out on to a lightly-floured surface and roll out to a thickness of $\frac{1}{8}$ to $\frac{1}{4}$ in (3–6 mm).

FURTHER READING

Stephen Davies and Alan Stewart, *Nutritional Medicine*, Pan, 1987

Derek Bryce-Smith and Liz Hodgkinson, *The Zinc Solution*, Century Arrow, 1986

Peter and Montse Bradford, *Cooking with Sea Vegetables*, Thorsons, 1985

Teruko and Seibin Arasaki, *Vegetables from the Sea*, Japan Publications Inc., 1983

Patrick Holford, *Vitamin Vitality*, Collins, 1985

Len Mervyn, *Dictionary of Vitamins*, Newman Turner, 1984

Andrew Stanway, *Trace Elements*, Thorsons, 1987

Alan Lewis, *Selenium*, Thorsons, 1983

The Liverpool Project, *Booker Health Report*, Liverpool City Council, 1985

Maryon Stewart, *Beat PMT Through Diet*, Ebury Press, 1987

Judy Ridgway, *Sprouting Beans and Seeds*, Century Arrow, 1984

BIBLIOGRAPHY

Recommended daily amounts of food energy and nutrients for groups of people in the United Kingdom. Report on Health and Social Subjects 15, HMSO, 1980

FAO, *Handbook on Human Nutritional Requirements*, HMSO, 1980

Report of a Joint FAO/WHO Expert group, *Requirements of Vitamin A, Iron, folate and vitamin B_{12}*, HMSO, 1989

US National Research Council Food and Nutrition Board, *Recommended Dietary Allowances*, National Academy of Science, 1980

A. A. Paul and D. A. T. Southgate, McCance and Widdowson's *The Composition of Foods*, 4th rev. ed., HMSO, 1980

S. P. Tan, R. W. Wenlock and D. H. Buss, *Immigrant Foods*, 2nd supplement to McCance and Widdowson's *The Composition of Foods*, HMSO, 1985

B. Holland, I. D. Unwin and D. H. Buss, *Cereals and Cereal Products*, 3rd supplement to McCance and Widdowson's *The Composition of Foods*, Royal Society of Chemistry and MAFF, 1989

Bernice K. Watt and Annabel L. Merrill, *Handbook of the Nutritional Contents of Foods*, for the US Department of Agriculture, Dover Publications Inc., 1985

Souci, Fachmann and Kraut, *Food Composition and Nutrition Tables 1986/7*, 3rd ed., Booker Health, 1988

MAFF, *Manual of Nutrition*, HMSO, 1985

MAFF, *Survey of Copper and Zinc in food*, Food Surveillance Paper Number 5, HMSO, 1981

R. W. Wenlock *et al.*, 'Trace nutrients. Iodine in British food', *British Journal of Nutrition* 1982, **47**, p. 381

G. A. Smart and J. C. Sherlock, 'Chromium in foods and the diet', *Food Additives and Contaminants*, 1985, **2**, pp. 139–47

L. M. Sivell *et al.*, 'Vitamin A activity in Foods of Animal Origin', *Journal of Food Agriculture*, 1984, **35**, pp. 931–39

R. W. Wenlock, D. H. Buss and E. J. Dixon, 'Trace nutrients. Manganese in British food', *British Journal of Nutrition*, 1979, **41**, p. 253

Janet Thorn *et al.*, 'Trace nutrients. Selenium in British food', *British Journal of Nutrition*, 1978, **39**, p. 391

MAFF, *Household Food Consumption and Expenditure 1985*, Annual Report of the National Food Survey Committee, HMSO, 1987

R. W. Wenlock, *The diets of British Schoolchildren*, DHSS, 1986

Nicola L. Bull, *The dietary habits of 15 to 25-year-olds*, MAFF, 1985

NACNE report, *Proposals for Nutritional Guidelines for Health Education in Britain*, Health Education Council, 1983

Report of a Joint FAO/IAEA/WHO Expert Committee, *Wholesomeness of Irradiated Food*, HMSO, 1981

Report on the Safety and Wholesomeness of Irradiated Foods, HMSO, 1986

Diet, Nutrition and Health, BMA, 1986

A. E. Bender, *The Importance of Vitamins to Human Health*, Fourth Kellogg Symposium, 1978

'Microwave Cooking of Vegetables. Ascorbic acid retention and palatability', *Journal of American Dietetic Association*, 1961, **39**, p. 61

A. E. Bender, *Food Processing and Nutrition*, Academic Press, 1978

'Do recommended daily dietary allowances stand up to scrutiny?', *Nutrition and Health*, 1983, **2**, pp. 105–9.

INDEX

This index is in word-by-word alphabetical order. Numbers in **bold** type indicate the main entry. FT: before numbers indicates that the food is listed as a source of specific vitamins or minerals in tables on those pages.

FOR THE BEST IN PAPERBACKS, LOOK FOR THE 🐧

In every corner of the world, on every subject under the sun, Penguin represents quality and variety – the very best in publishing today.

For complete information about books available from Penguin – including Puffins, Penguin Classics and Arkana – and how to order them, write to us at the appropriate address below. Please note that for copyright reasons the selection of books varies from country to country.

In the United Kingdom: Please write to *Dept E.P., Penguin Books Ltd, Harmondsworth, Middlesex, UB7 0DA.*

If you have any difficulty in obtaining a title, please send your order with the correct money, plus ten per cent for postage and packaging, to *PO Box No 11, West Drayton, Middlesex*

In the United States: Please write to *Dept BA, Penguin, 299 Murray Hill Parkway, East Rutherford, New Jersey 07073*

In Canada: Please write to *Penguin Books Canada Ltd, 2801 John Street, Markham, Ontario L3R 1B4*

In Australia: Please write to the *Marketing Department, Penguin Books Australia Ltd, P.O. Box 257, Ringwood, Victoria 3134*

In New Zealand: Please write to the *Marketing Department, Penguin Books (NZ) Ltd, Private Bag, Takapuna, Auckland 9*

In India: Please write to *Penguin Overseas Ltd, 706 Eros Apartments, 56 Nehru Place, New Delhi, 110019*

In the Netherlands: Please write to *Penguin Books Netherlands B.V., Postbus 195, NL–1380AD Weesp*

In West Germany: Please write to *Penguin Books Ltd, Friedrichstrasse 10–12, D–6000 Frankfurt/Main 1*

In Spain: Please write to *Longman Penguin España, Calle San Nicolas 15, E–28013 Madrid*

In Italy: Please write to *Penguin Italia s.r.l., Via Como 4, I-20096 Pioltello (Milano)*

In France: Please write to *Penguin Books Ltd, 39 Rue de Montmorency, F-75003 Paris*

In Japan: Please write to *Longman Penguin Japan Co Ltd, Yamaguchi Building, 2–12–9 Kanda Jimbocho, Chiyoda-Ku, Tokyo 101*

Traditional Jamaican Cookery Norma Benghiat

Reflecting Arawak, Spanish, African, Jewish, English, French, East Indian and Chinese influences, the exciting recipes in this definitive book range from the lavish eating of the old plantocracy to imaginative and ingenious slave and peasant dishes.

Cooking in a Bedsit Katharine Whitehorn

Practical and light-hearted, the perfect book for those cooking in limited space, with little time and less money – problems that can easily be surmounted with imagination, common sense and a great deal of news-paper. 'All parents with bedsitter children should send them a copy' – *Observer*

The Beginner's Cookery Book Betty Falk

Revised and updated, this book is for aspiring cooks of all ages who want to make appetizing and interesting meals without too much fuss. With an emphasis on healthy eating, this is the ideal starting point for would-be cooks.

Jane Grigson's Fruit Book

Fruit is colourful, refreshing and life-enhancing; this book shows how it can also be absolutely delicious in meringues or compotes, soups or pies.

Fast Food for Vegetarians Janette Marshall

Packed with ideas for healthy, delicious dishes from Caribbean vegetables to rose-water baklava, this stimulating book proves that fast food does not have to mean junk food.

Malaysian Cookery Rafi Fernandez

A step-by-step guide to the intoxicating, fragrant, colourful cuisine of Malaysia: the origins of its three distinct culinary strands, traditional cooking techniques and customs, where to buy the more exotic ingredients – and a mouthwatering selection of recipes.

FOR THE BEST IN PAPERBACKS, LOOK FOR THE 🐧

FOOD AND COOKING IN PENGUIN

The Fratelli Camisa Cookery Book   Elizabeth Camisa

From antipasti to zabaglione, from the origins of gorgonzola to the storage of salami, an indispensable guide to real Italian home cooking from Elizabeth Camisa of the famous Fratelli Camisa delicatessen in Soho's Berwick Street.

A Table in Tuscany   Leslie Forbes

With authentic recipes and beautiful illustrations, artist and cook Leslie Forbes evokes the rich flavour of Tuscany, from its Renaissance palaces to its robust red Chianti. More than a cookery book and more than mere travel writing, *A Table in Tuscany* is a culinary odyssey.

The Food and Cooking of Eastern Europe   Lesley Chamberlain

Diverse, appetizing and often surprisingly sophisticated, the cuisine of Eastern Europe goes far beyond the goulash and beetroot soup familiar to the West. From the refreshing fruit soups of Hungary to the fish dishes of Dalmatia, this is a fascinating tour of Eastern gastronomy.

Out to Lunch   Paul Levy

Gloriously entertaining essays from Britain's best-known writer on food and drink as he eats out around the world. Whether you want to know more about truffle-hunting, cheeses, aphrodisiacs or the great American sandwich, or whether people actually do eat dogs in Macao, all the answers are here.

The Penguin Book of Jams, Pickles and Chutneys   David and Rose Mabey

'An excellent book; practical, personal and suggestive, every recipe's clearly the result of real experience and written with great charm' – *The Times*

More Easy Cooking for One or Two   Louise Davies

This charming book, full of ideas and easy recipes, offers even the novice cook good wholesome food with the minimum of effort.